THE TWELFTH

THE TWELFTH

by

J. K. STANFORD

illustrated by

V. H. DRUMMOND

FABER & FABER LIMITED
24 Russell Square
London

First published in Mcmxliv
by Faber and Faber Limited
24 Russell Square London W.C. 1
Second impression March Mcmxlv
Third impression October Mcmxlv
Fourth impression October Mcmxlvi
Fifth impression March Mcmxlviii
Sixth impression May Mcml
Seventh impression February Mcmliii
Printed in Great Britain by
R. MacLehose and Company Limited
The University Press Glasgow

CONTENTS

I

GEORGE PROTERON

"That?" said the Club secretary, as he followed his guest's eyes across the smoking-room. "Oh, that's old George Proteron: they say he's still one of the ten or twelve best shots in the Kingdom!"

"Proteron?" queried Charles Savile; "any relation of the Bill Proteron who used to be Master of the Blankman? *He* was a bit of a menace when I used to hunt with them."

"Yes, I believe they're half-brothers, and haven't spoken for thirty years. Bill thinks a fox is sacred except when he's after it, whereas if old George P. ever saw a fox in his part of Cambridgeshire, he'd write to his member and the County Council and *The Times* about it and put down strychnine all over the estate as if it was artificial manure...! He only lives for shooting on the largest possible scale. We call him here the old Grouse-cock!"

The stout baldish little man with the scarlet face, who had been staring fiercely at the papers on the big centre-table of the smoking-room, seized one, chuckled a swift order at a waiter, and strutted away towards the third fire-place. His alert carriage, the bristling red eyebrows above the pink-brown eyes, the rich heather-mixture tweeds and grey spats, all set off by that commanding beak of a nose, made plain to Charles Savile how he had come by his nickname. One glance from him was enough to deter a nervous country-member from any designs on his favourite arm-chair, into which the Grouse-cock settled as of ancient right. He gave a swift challenging look round the room, then wrapped himself in the *Squire* and the smoke of his cigar.

"Apt enough name for him: he must be Bill Proteron's brother all right," said Charles Savile. "Tell me some more about him." He knew his host, Martin Kenyon, was a walking *Who's Who* of the twelve hundred members of the Qu'hais' Club, and was reputed to know them all by name, sight, foible and even overdraft.

Martin Kenyon mused for a moment, and then began:

"Colonel the Honourable George Hysteron-Proteron, C.B., J.P., a marvellous old boy and one of the plagues of my humble existence. Born (I have little doubt) in wedlock, though I don't know the details. Aged 68. Educated: Eton, the Black Scots, and the Badminton Library. Fought with Matabeles, Chins, Boers, French landladies (where he got a C.B. as Hirings Officer, or Billeting Officer, or something in 1918), *and* with every ruddy committee we've ever had here. Unmarried (more's the pity, as it might keep him away from this place). Clubs: Boodle's, this one, and, I suspect, the Gamekeeper's Benevolent. Recreations: shooting, shooting, and vintage port. Family seat: Five Mile Wallop (which he has somehow let at a fabulous rent while retaining all the shooting). Has travelled extensively in all the best game-counties and shot about 200,000 head. Heir: a nephew, rumoured to be in quod at this moment for dangerous driving on the Kingston By-pass. . . . That's about the lot, I think!"

"Where does the money come from?"

"I really don't know. Most of it goes with the eldest brother, Lord Parable. George and Bill both seem to have a bit, but I know for years they were cherishing a very rich but invalid Hysteron aunt in Suffolk, which was why they never spoke. And then (would you believe it?) she died and left it in equal shares to the R.S.P.C.A. and the Society for the Abolition of Blood-sports. All Bill and George Proteron inherited was a five-page sermon on 'Cruelty' in her own unique handwriting, and a framed quotation from Coleridge about 'Loving best both man and bird and beast' which used to hang in her bathroom. Oh, yes! . . . *and* a suggestion that if George felt impelled to shoot birds, he ought at least to send them to a museum!" Charles spluttered into his coffee cup.

"How divine! Can't you see the B.M. trustees in Cromwell Road suddenly confronted with two hundred gift cock-pheasants on a Monday morning! Tell me more . . . is he really as fine a shot as all that?"

"Is he not? . . . though I'm blowed if I know how he does it. Years ago, when I was still in the army, he asked me to shoot with him once when he had Tattenhall. He quite staggered me! he hardly missed a bird before lunch, which for him meant beer and curry and stilton. He then drew out an enormous silver-topped hunting-flask holding about a pint of port, and scoffed the lot, except about a thimbleful he gave his head-keeper while they were discussing the afternoon drives. . . .

"At the next stand it was blowing a gale and we were in a dip below a young larch covert on the side of a hill. We had a series of absolute snorters over us which no one else could touch, and which looked like starlings to me. But old George Proteron must have been seeing 'em by then twice as large as life, for he hardly missed one, and shot like a dream until he knocked himself out with a real high cock-pheasant which landed on his head when he was changing guns. . . . We never knew whether it was the concussion or the port that did him in that day. Anyway, he lay in state in the game-cart most of the afternoon,

just breathing, and all among the game, and when he came to, was very indignant to discover how little the rest of us had shot."

"He sounds a bit of a *marcheur*," murmured Charles Savile, "like his half-brother, Bill, who used to curse the heads off all of us with the Blankman. Do you get a stream of stuff in the Club complaint-book from the old bird?"

"Yes, a fair bit and letters to the Committee, calling down fire and sword on me. That's one of the reasons, apart from his looks, why we call him the Grouse-cock. He used to insist on having grouse for

9

luncheon, 'properly hung too, young man,' almost all the year round except in early August, when he was certain they must be poached! He stopped that, though, two years ago when a pal of his killed himself by eating cold storage partridges in June. It came out at the inquest that they hung on a hook outside the shop all day and went back into the frig. at night, so that by June they were in, well, shall we say, an interesting condition? . . .

"He's an awful old nuisance too, because he will practise changing guns with his valet in his bedroom. He must have broken a dozen or more electric light bulbs a year doing that."

"Politics?" queried Charles.

"Well, true-blue Tory, or magenta die-hard, whichever you like to call it. There'll always be someone to ask George Proteron out shooting, even under Stalin. If ever the social revolution comes off, you'll find George on the last day of it, in the very best butt on Moy or Wemmergill, with three guns and two loaders, making a last stand, and mowing down the proletariat who dare to want access to moorlands!"

"Does he ever read anything?" asked Charles. He was beginning to like the Grouse-cock, who seemed to run so true to form.

"Very little. He's almost completely illiterate, though he keeps a most elaborate game-book, now in its twentieth volume. He reads *The Times*, or at any rate goes to sleep under it for half an hour a day; the *Squire*, the *Shooting World*, and the racing news in the evening paper. . . . I know he once wrote to *The Times*, because he rang me up and asked me how to spell 'self-opinionated'. I saw the letter next day, and George was raving because they'd cut out his most abusive paragraph which contained two split infinitives. . . . But now and again he does burst into print to contradict someone on a matter of shooting history. You know the sort of thing?

"'*I should like to point out to your correspondent that the record bag on Blubergill on Aug. 23rd, 1929, was not 1011 brace, but 1013½ brace and one snipe. The wind was blowing strongly from the S.S.W. all day and not from the S.E. as imagined by your correspondent. The bag would have been even larger but for the fact that Colonel the Hon. G. Hysteron-Proteron did not shoot after luncheon, owing to the death of an aunt.*

I enclose my card and remain,

                                 Yours, etc.,

                                         Venator.'

"Lovely!" murmured Charles. "I know the sort: they're the woof of history. Shooting-shop is even more solemn than golf-shop when it comes to figures. But, Martin, why, oh why, that last sentence? I can't really see your friend George laying down his arms, in the middle of a record day on a moor like that, merely out of sorrow for a dead aunt?"

"Nor can I," said Martin Kenyon. "But by what I once heard he'd been beating it up a bit overnight, when he heard she'd passed on, and when he received Bill Proteron's frenzied wire at lunch-time telling him all about the R.S.P.C.A. legacy, and the Blood-sports and what not, it was just too much for him and his gun-headache won hands down!"

II

BLOOD-SPORTS

"We *are* a queer race," mused Charles, lighting another cigarette. "Nobody ever understood what Wilde meant when he wrote:

'for all men slay the thing they love.'

"But we bring up millions of grouse and partridges and pheasants solely in order to amuse ourselves by killing them, and all the time we write and talk of our victims, and have pictures painted of them in their last moments, with a wealth of sentimental fellow-feeling, in which no trace of our intended or actual treachery to them ever appears. Supposing we diverted one-tenth of the money we spend on improving the stock of grouse or deer to improving the stock of slum-children? . . . But I suppose that's blasphemy in the Qu'hais' Club, ain't it, Martin? . . .

"But it's really the treachery I never can get over. When I was trying to farm down in Hampshire, I used to hate watching my lambs and calves eating their way steadily nearer the butcher day by day. I gave it up at last because it seemed such a cad's trick to betray them one fine morning for thirty pieces of silver. They were such jolly little brutes!"

"Oh, come! come! Charles! you mustn't carry it as far as that, especially after lunch in this place! You'll be giving the hens their eggs back next, in order not to be accused of infanticide!"

11

"I know, it *is* silly of me. But there are squads of 'em now-a-days, the poet-shooters who shoot hard three or four days a week all the season and then rhapsodize about the thrill it gives them to see the surviving partridges chasing each other about the fields in February, or dilate on their faithfulness to their newly-hatched young in June. If you told those chaps they were sadists for six months a year, they'd be really hurt and annoyed. If you compared them to this chap, Hitler, who signs a Non-Aggression Pact with his prospective victim,

12

which he breaks at the moment it suits him, they'd not only never speak to you again, but they'd never even see what you're driving at!"

"Ye—es," assented Martin Kenyon. "I dare say you're right, and this is a cock-eyed world. Still, I have a sneaking admiration for old George Proteron, who lives his life dominating his native ground, and doesn't give a damn for anyone. He's as fiercely self-centred and prickly as a porcupine. They say he shot old Sam Staff, his keeper, last year, partridge-driving. He killed a bird as it topped the fence, killed a dog fifty yards out on the other side, and peppered old Staff, who'd been his head-man for thirty-five years, in both gaiters, all with the same barrel. Sam was prepared to make a row about it, but he got no change at all. He nearly got sacked for getting in the way, and all the sympathy he collected was a dose of iodine, the reversion of George's first field-dressing (retained since 1914) and the assurance that George had never shot a keeper in the last fifty years, which proved this one must be a b——y fool!"

Charles went on musing.

"What happens", he asked, "to the George Proterons of this world in the next? Are they glued eternally to electric shooting seats, and do they whirl round and round in space presenting red-hot gun-barrels at asbestos birds which never never fall? Is that about it?"

Martin nodded.

"If there is any justice in this world or the next, George will be unpaid secretary of my club and have to act on all my flaming complaints. And I shall be paid chairman of the house committee with plenary powers to kick him round the silence room. But let us drop these wishful speculations."

"Do you remember", asked Charles irrelevantly, "Saki's remark about the embarrassment one would feel at the prospect of meeting in the next life a shoal of whitebait one had last known at Prince's. Restaurant? Your friend George may have a bit coming to him one day on those lines. Look at him! He's away!"

Both men glanced across the room. Colonel Proteron had fallen on sleep, with the new *Squire* open at "Prospects for the Twelfth" shielding his ample waistcoat. Bolt upright, in a much less comfortable chair just behind him, sat a nervous country-member who was only up for the day, and was particularly anxious to read an article in the journal on harvest-mice. He was watching the *Squire* hungrily as it

15

rose and fell and wishing he had the nerve to tip-toe across and lay hands on it.

On the other side of the fireplace, protected from a chill by the new *Country Life*, reposed an ex-Governor of the Central Provinces. His faint purring was likely at any moment to merge into that larger other sound which had earned for him the club-name of the Minute Gun. For Sir Owen had lunched that day with appetite. It was one of the two days a week on which the Qu'hais' peripatetic curry-chef, who also ministered to the New Oriental and the In-and-Out, had plied his art at home. Sir Owen was for the moment in Paradise or back, at any rate, in Jubbulpore about 1906, which was not, in retrospect, so very far away.

Martin Kenyon rose.

"Come on, Charles! let's go and play bridge! It's a horrible pastime in London on a July afternoon, but I've got a committee at 4.15, so I'm on duty. Away we go, and for heaven's sake 'tread light o'er the dead in the valley'!"

They tip-toed out. The nervous country-member, who had to kill time somehow while his wife was encased in a green mud-pack at Catherine Savernake's, had given up hope of the *Squire*, and though a distinguished naturalist, was endeavouring to console himself with an article entitled "My Baby Otters" in one of the evening newspapers. He guessed the danger he ran of attempting to rob a fellow-member of his spoils.

Even the Club fly, which had got in by accident three days before while the room was being aired, felt that it was as much as his life was worth to make an alighting ground of that aristocratic countenance, so subtly vermilioned by vintage port, the sun and breezes of all the best game-counties, and perhaps a tinge of blood-pressure. He had touched down there for a brief moment on his first day in the Club, and the blisters on the soles of his feet, where he had been scalded, were still a vivid memory and a warning. Moreover, the Colonel's sneeze, when at last his defences had come into action, had nearly blown him into the fireplace. So he balanced himself upside-down on the mirror above the third mantelpiece and polished himself gingerly with his hind-legs, wondering why it was so much more fun on that pane of glass, where one could see backwards, than it was on the great windows of the smoking-room with their eternal view out over the street which he felt he would never roam again.

III

ALFRED LEICESTER

A thin weather-beaten man in a neat dark-blue suit, with a huge Adam's apple jutting out of his white collar, tip-toed into the room and stood at ease beside the old waiter near the coffee-table. He was Colonel Proteron's valet-loader-chauffeur, and he knew he had no business to be there in the smoking-room at all.

"Just a spot of A.R.P., Smiler boy," he whispered to the gloomy waiter, who had raised his eyebrows. "My bloke under control *and* that cigar of his? That's all I come for."

Alfred Leicester had served his time as a batman in the 59th, the famous first battalion of the "Eggs and Dregs". Not only that, but for seven years he had acted as conscience and memory to the equally famous Major Bunworrie, "Old Skinful ", as he had been affectionately known half over India and the Middle East, and in those seven years, never once, winter or summer, had he failed in his duty at Lights Out to go round and extinguish his major, lest he should set himself or his mess-kit or the barracks on fire with what remained of his cigar.

"A.R.P.?" said the gloomy waiter, casting a glance towards the third fire-place: Colonel Proteron's abandoned cheroot was smoking quietly to itself in the great silver ash-tray. "Pass, Alfie, and all's well! The cigar's all right, though your bloke looked a bit incandescent when he came in: I thought he was going to catch fire at any moment."

"Ah!" said Alfred Leicester meaningly: "he's had a very worrying morning." He looked carefully at the recumbent form. "He seems nicely damped down now. I want to get away."

"Off you go, then," said the gloomy waiter. "And remember if you can get three's on 'Ushaby Baby you can put 'arf a crack on for me. That 'orse 'asn't run straight all this season, and as both the *News* and *Star* says 'e's out of 'is class today, I reckon this must be 'is afternoon off!"

"Yes," said the thin man, "but was Lord Skewbald in to lunch to-day?"

16

"Not 'im, not when 'e's got even a dead one running. He and your bloke lunched together on Monday, Alfie, but we couldn't get nothing except that they were shooting at the same place on the Twelfth and that 'e was fed up with losing money on three-year-olds, and was going to pawn 'is stud. But 'e wouldn't be likely to give anything away about 'Ushaby to the Colonel, would he?"

"How so?" Alfred Leicester was clearly on his dignity.

"Well, I'm told your bloke nearly shot 'im at Campsey last year in a fracass over a woodcock, so Lord Skewbald would 'ardly be likely to throw money at him, would 'e?"

"Fracass to you, Smiler," said Alfred loftily. "You waiters listen to too much gossip. There was a lot of lead flying about that afternoon, but me and the Colonel are as safe as anyone I've seen. We *have* to be in the class we're in. What happened was, it came out at lunch that the Colonel and Old Skewbald" (I am sorry to say that this was Lord Charles Casserole's pantry-name in the Club) "had each of 'em shot 49½ couple of woodcock that season, and both was bursting to get his century that day. There was a bet on!"

"And who won?"

"Neither of 'em, though they got off six barrels at it between 'em. And afterwards each swore he couldn't hold straight on account of the curtain of fire put down by the other beggar. It was a most unfortunate ending to the season."

"Well, be that as it may, Alfie," (the gloomy waiter had served in an embassy till his corns and his temper proved too much for him), "and putting two and two together, I reckon 'Ushaby's a fair price at threes. . . . Off you go, and if the old Cock does start creatin', I'll say you've gone round to the laundry to see about his dress-shirts. Meanwhile R.I.P.!"

The thin man slid away and peace enveloped the great smoking-room.

IV

REVERIE OF A QU'HAI

It was, of course, grossly incorrect to assume that Colonel Proteron was asleep. He had read somewhere of a famous man who had been able to add at least two hours to his working-day by half-an-hour's meditation with his eyes closed after luncheon; and though the Colonel's own working-day might perhaps have been considered almost a whole holiday by captious critics, he had adopted the practice and

proved it to be of benefit. So now, as he lay with his bosom rising and falling beneath "Prospects for the Twelfth" and "Some Outstanding Two-year-olds", he was thinking of the sun on leagues of cloud-shadowed heather and of dark shapes coming suddenly out of a fold in the moor and sweeping towards him to their doom, as nothing could stop them from doing in a fortnight's time. He was thinking too of brown shapes whirring and swerving over belts of October larch above his upturned face, and of long-tailed forms a month later shimmering in copper and green and brown, which would sail high over him on strong set wings in that moment before he extinguished them so adroitly for ever.

The film of memory rolled on. Pack after pack, covey after covey, bird after bird came sweeping towards him, him the inexorable whose

18

practised hand took such toll of them all. His mind was a jumble of figures and places and, above all, of records: the year they broke all the figures even for Bows, the year Jerry Gherkin had Clamergill when in a thundering bad season they averaged 300 brace a day all through August; that day at Swarraton where he had 47 birds down in the first drive, and then it blew such a gale for the rest of the day that the head-keeper got tipsy at luncheon out of chagrin and dared to address him as "Uncle George"; the Foxburrow stand at Chippingham where he and H.R.H. (as he was then, God bless him!) had 302 birds down between them; the day he had wiped the old Earl's eye four times running when he was in the back row at the Clump and had never been asked again; the drive on Washam where he ought to have had 59 grouse in 67 cartridges, in October too! but for an infernal scoundrel of a parson in the next butt whose spaniel had sneaked five birds from under his nose during the drive; the day at Eusden in January when they shot so many cock-pheasants before luncheon that everyone ran out of cart-ridges and they had to send down to a little ironmonger's in the village.

And dominating them all, that dreadful day near Tomintoul when an American had asked him to shoot and had brought all his women-folk out, including even one who was armed with a 20-bore.

Poor George Proteron! he had been so busy and anxious waiting to be shot all day that he had barely been able to shoot anything himself at all. In the first drive after luncheon he had even invited his host's daughter, Madeleine Cranmer, into his butt as a sort of hostage, a quite unheard-of thing for George Proteron to do, for he did not mind women sharing one's bed and board, but never, damn it all, one's butt. He had done so, however, feeling vaguely that just as dog does not eat dog, so woman would not shoot woman.

But it was no use. For all his precautions he had had a very poor drive when it ought to have been a really killing one. For what with Madeleine Cranmer yattering and making eyes at old Alfred Leicester (whom she would describe as "the Kurnel's stand-in"), and what with her yellow curls and blue jumper, not to mention her blood-red nails and lips, the grouse had shied away from his butt as if it had been the Eddystone. She had spent her time eating grapes and expectorating the pips in between questions about the number of "shells per annum" he got through, and what with her incessant "Say, Kurnel," she had nearly driven him crazy.

" ... *deliberately ejecting two brass cases almost into her scarlet mouth.*"

Old Alfred had done his best, of course, in his blundering way to ease the strain, for Alfred was a faithful servant. He had breathed advice and onions all over her till the birds started to come, and, after that, had hustled her up against the ropes, as it were, and given her several sharp jabs over the heart with his elbow while changing guns, as well as interrupting one question by deliberately ejecting two brass cases almost into her scarlet mouth. But what good had that done?

"Say, Kurnel," (George could hear her voice now). "Your stand-in's becoming quite a cave-man back here! Why not come off the stage for a brief spell and let poor Alfie go have a bang?"

George Proteron had even tried as a last resort to drug her with the contents of his famous flask, but all she said was: "Gee! I never dreamed you had bottle-parties in these cunning little hide-outs. But not for this baby, thanks! I never use hard liquor before sundown!"

Yes, it had been a most dreadful day, and though George had gone to it quietly bent on showing these Americans what the best people in the old country could accomplish on a moor, he could still hardly look at the figures in his game-book. And both he and Alfred Leicester still winced and blushed in memory at the thought of their innocence at bay in a butt with a female so brazen.

Somehow the future of shooting seemed all dark and comfortless: syndicates everywhere of bookmakers and haberdashers and stockbrokers, expecting you to pay £200 a gun for what people had been only too glad to invite you to do for forty years; poachers in gangs in motor-cars; supertax and the breaking up of the great preserves where it had been as much as a farmer's lease was worth to put a field down to grass; and all this infernal nonsense about the public having access to mountains. Heaven alone knew what we were coming to with a Government so weak-kneed as to ask Gandhi to Viceregal Lodge, which spent the rest of its time feeding propitiatory buns to that rascally upstart in Berlin. Yes, it was a grim outlook, no privilege or privacy for a gentleman anywhere.

He could still barely think of that day (it had been hushed up in his game-journal) when he had climbed to the top-butt on the Rigs at Glenconnan which was always such a grand butt in an east wind. There he had discovered a picnic-party of three spinsters (hikers they seemed to call them now), eating bloater-paste and drinking tea under a large red umbrella in this almost hallowed structure from which thousands of cartridges had been fired by some of the best shots and greatest noblemen of their time.

Even old Alfred Leicester that day had nearly "blown a valve", in his own phrase, when the party had calmly told him to sit down and wait as they weren't ready yet, and would the other old gentleman like a nice cup of tea?

George had walked away fuming. He had never known how Alfred had managed to get rid of those women, whether by threats or entreaty or improper suggestions, but gone they had at last, quacking loudly and indignantly over the march, thank God! just before the beaters started and the drive developed.

George had been so upset that he had missed four or five quite reasonable birds at the start of the drive, and one way and another that sort of incident was abominably bad for one's nerves when, to shoot really well, you had to be as calm as fate with no other cares in the world. Later his doctor had warned him about blood-pressures, and suggested that he "ought to put the muzzle on a bit tighter, especially over port".

Muzzle himself! As if he, George Proteron, had ever done it in sixty-five years! And was not the recipe for long life in Australia to drink a bottle of port every night and ride for two hours every morning before breakfast? Though, of course, he himself for years had had to cut out the second part of the recipe, with all these motors on the roads.

But as for these mealy-mouthed *babus* they made major-generals nowadays, all barley-water and staff-jargon about "low priorities", and "commitments ", and "target-figures for production", and "keeping themselves in the tactical picture ", and "operational necessities", and "discussions on a high level" and "armoured components", they could go and muzzle themselves, and a good job too! One had never used phrases like that in the Old Army, to begin with because nobody would have known how to spell them.

But now it was all this new democratic army of young Belisha's, all Y.M.C.A. and welfare, or "buns and bonhomie", as someone had phrased it, with long hair and no discipline and vehicles littering the roads for miles like a Bank Holiday. You could mark his words: they would be getting themselves into a most preposterous tangle some day if they ever went into action, which God forbid! Democratic army, indeed!

A faint snort at this point might conceivably have been mistaken by the uninstructed for a snore.

But the worst possible event of all, in this bleak outlook, had happened that very day. It was bad enough to have a young orphan nephew, Rupert Pilimore, who actually talked about "scatter-guns" and did not seem likely ever to rise above ferreting; who trapesed all over the kingdom from swimming-pool to roadhouse, from roadhouse to Mayfair, like a human torpedo, in a long low red oval car, with no hood and no silencer, his hair streaming in the wind and some unutterable young thing chattering beside him.

That was bad enough. But when it came to his knocking down municipal lamp-posts when unlicensed and uninsured, and then wiring for his Uncle George to come and bail himself and the wretched girl out, then it was not only a gross scandal, but absolutely intolerable. And on this occasion his companion, clad in nothing but a bathing-dress, a mackintosh and a spotted scarf round her head, had been none other than the very Madeleine Cranmer with the blood-red nails who had so miserably spoilt his day's sport at Tomintoul.

But for once the ties of blood had held, and he, Colonel the Honourable George Hysteron-Proteron, had made Alfred Leicester drive him down to that police station on the edge of the Kingston By-pass; where almost the last straw had been his interview with a most supercilious young policeman in plain clothes, who had actually kept George standing while he lounged at a table and took notes with a cigarette in his mouth. "Proteron, George, eh? Address: Qu'hais' Club, St. James's. Occupation?"

As if a gentleman of sixty-eight had any other occupation but just being a gentleman!

"Gentleman".

"Yes, they all call themselves that. Any other?"

"Lately commanding the Loyal Highlanders".

He was not going to speak of the Black Scots to this unkempt lout with his short grimy fingernails and long greasy hair.

"Oh, were you? I was in the Irish Guards myself for a year!"

The Colonel bit back the words that came seething to his lips while his complexion rushed up and took possession of his forehead. To be patronized and insulted by a young clodhopper to whom the Guards had failed to teach either manners or cleanliness! The young man consulted his book again.

"Means?"

He supposed one had means, but one never knew from day to day what they were. One left all that to one's man of business and the bank, and precious little seemed to trickle through by the time they had filled up all the infernal forms and taken their own and the Government's whack. What was the phrase they always used: "independent"?

"Come on!" said the young policeman impatiently. "Means of livelihood? When we were sending the telegram to you, the young female described you as an 'ace bird-shooter'. But that can't be all. How do you earn your living?"

Ace bird-shooter indeed! and he among the premier gameshots of the last twenty-five years. Indignation almost reduced the poor Colonel to complete speechlessness, but somehow at last his clothes and his temper had over-awed the police station and he had been allowed to see the precious pair, both dressed in mackintoshes and bathing-dresses, and twittering together on a bench in the same cell, mark you, like a brace of rascally budgerigars.

The walls of the station rang while he told them what he thought of them, with pauses for breath. Finally, when they had also heard all he had intended for the young policeman, they had been duly enlarged on £200 bail and had departed, still twittering, in what was left of the car and an aura of scent and cheap tobacco-smoke.

"Cheeribye, Uncle George! and thanks most terribly!"

"Okey-doke, Kurnel, and ta very much for the bail. Hope I may be able to do the same for you one day!"

The Colonel's nerves had been rasped by this last farewell, as never before in their long history, especially with two of those scoundrels of peelers grinning behind him in the station door-way. To be patronized by them was bad enough, but the idea of himself, George Hysteron-Proteron, ever being bailed out by that brazen hussy with her crimson lips and finger-nails *and*, as he had always suspected and now knew for certain, crimson toe-nails as well, was too much for anyone. He had stumped back into his car and sat bolt upright with his hands on his knees all the way back to London, so that Alfred Leicester had looked at him quite anxiously once or twice and attempted no conversation at all. Normally his master's complexion blended admirably with his gray bowler hat, but now its usual vinous-pink was a mottled plum colour in savage contrast to his auburn eyebrows.

Yes, it had been a really bad morning. The mere recollection of it wrung from the Colonel a snort which shook him from head to foot and almost silenced the Minute Gun, who was sullenly firing in the opposite arm-chair.

V

PERCHANCE TO DREAM

It was about four o'clock and Martin Kenyon was just saying goodbye to his guest in the office before the committee meeting. He and Charles Savile had won £2 more or less imperceptibly from an ex-Resident of the Solomon Islands and a wealthy bookmaker who, in retirement, rather fancied his bridge but had an incurable tendency, the result of years of inhibition on the course, to try a flutter.

They were just leaving the office when the Assistant Secretary, Mr. Fairy, who had graduated from the post of still-room apprentice in the long ago, tip-toed in, pale and agitated.

"I'm sorry, Major," he gasped, "but I've just been in the smoking-room, and I don't like the look of Colonel Proteron at all!"

"I never did!" said Martin Kenyon breezily, "but I've never let that worry me. One get's used to it!"

He smiled with the brazen frankness which had so often endeared him to his hard-pressed staff. For the last twenty years Martin Kenyon had made a point at least three times a day of saying and doing exactly what occurred to him, as a spiritual exercise. It had won him in less than three years of war, as his regiment remembered with delight, two M.C.'s, a D.S.O., a Croix de Guerre, a battalion at the age of twenty-eight, and then, what everyone had foreseen, a bar to his bowler hat, on the second occasion after a pitched battle with his Corps Commander. After he had "taken felt", no one knew why he had settled down so long in his cloistered existence. Some hinted he was making £1,000 a year out of the members at bridge. Others thought it must be an obscure religious penance. Some darkly suspected him of wanting local colour for a novel.

But poor Mr. Fairy was quite shocked by his flippancy.

"But it isn't that, sir! It's his colour: he's hardly breathing and he doesn't look at all right in himself. James-the-Waiter thought he was dying!"

"Oh, Lord!" said Martin. "We'd better come along then!" Too many members were waiting at ease on death in a Club which he had once nicknamed the "Sporting and Rheumatic", but so far they had all died in their beds. A demise in the smoking-room, hushed up though it would be, would have a most lowering effect on the bar and the luncheon receipts, which were among the solid bulwarks of the Club's finances.

"Got a stretcher, Fairy?" he asked as the three raced upstairs to the smoking-room.

"The A.R.P. one is in attendance," murmured the faithful assistant.

Colonel Proteron certainly did look bad. His eyes were closed, he was just breathing, and the scarlet had fled from his face and forehead and left it and his cheeks strangely mottled with little red threads of veins. The ex-Governor of the Central Provinces, who had just fallen from the heaven of his dream and was rubbing his eyes, was gazing furtively at his neighbour as if he looked too bad to be true.

Martin bent over the Colonel, and then called Charles aside.

"It's a stroke, by the look of it. Snaffle that waiter, Charles, and let's

27

get him along quietly to his own room before the M.O. comes. He's for it if we don't look out."

Gingerly they eased the lax form on to the stretcher and moved towards the door. Sir Owen stood up, uncertain whether he should stand to attention or merely bow. Was another link with the past being severed before his eyes?

For Sir Owen had known George Proteron for over forty years, in fact since he was a junior captain. It was himself and poor "Plukes" Enderby (afterwards such a brilliant member of the Viceroy's Council) who had done their best, in their hot manhood and for a wager, to drink George under the table one September night at the Nagpur Club. They had agreed to drink alternate drinks against each of his, so that George was two to their one throughout the evening.

The attempt had failed most miserably: and when, in fact, they had tottered off to bed, breathing fire and singing songs of Araby, of which the mere recollection made Sir Owen blush,

relicta non bene palmula,

or whatever it was, they had left George Proteron, flushed and just a little argumentative about shooting statistics, in full possession of the stricken field.

Nor was that all. Poor "Plukes" had kept to his bed next day, but when Sir Owen himself had crept wanly down at ten that morning, feeling as though he had been pole-axed, he had found George Proteron rosy with exercise and as fresh as a daisy, eating curried eggs and washing them down with ale.

His greeting, too, had been entirely typical. "You *are* a miserable pair of lazy devils! I've been out since six this morning and shot thirty couple of snipe!"

But now . . . the blind fury had come with her abhorred shears and George's sins had found him out. So Sir Owen stood while the stretcher passed him and decided, in that moment, to cut out his second sherry before luncheon and his after-dinner glass of port and to double his morning exercises in the bathroom.

The cortège passed through the door towards the back of the Club, headed by Charles and the gloomy waiter, who managed to preserve admirably the funereal appearance which had won him his pantry-name of Smiler. He did not really feel sorry, for the Colonel had bitten him hard and often in the last twenty years, and inwardly he was hoping that Alfred Leicester would be back swiftly from his commission agents, and that his own duties would permit him to pop down to the tape in the hall and discover the fate of Hushaby Baby. He did not altogether trust Alfred Leicester over starting-prices.

They laid the Colonel on his bed, loosened his collar and waistcoat and covered him with a blanket. Mr. Fairy scuttled away to telephone for a doctor.

"Hold the fort, Charles, old boy!" said Martin. "I *must* go and break it to my committee and get them to put off that blasted meeting. I won't be five minutes, and the Doctor should be here by then!"

VI

BEDROOM SCENE

Left to himself, Charles Savile glanced curiously round the room. There were the Colonel's three Purdeys and a couple of rookrifles gleaming in a tall mahogany case beside the washstand. Two leather gun-cases and two vast cartridge magazines, worn with travel and covered with innumerable labels, were in a corner, alongside the Colonel's capacious leather shooting-seat with its aluminium fittings. On a great rack shone, tier by tier, his seventeen pairs of boots and shoes, the lowest row dedicated to well-greased ankle-boots with their anklets around them. There was something marvellously polished and perdurable about this congregation of footwear, on which it seemed time could lay no decaying finger.

The bookcase did not hold many books: the Badminton Library, *Autumns in Aberdeenshire, Thirty Years of Sport in Central India, High Pheasants in Theory and Practice, The Keeper's Book,* a manual of game-rearing, *The Improvement of Partridge Manors,* and *The Diary of Colonel Peter Hawker.* Beside them were the twenty stout volumes of the Colonel's own shooting-journal, in red leather stamped with his full name in gold. The pictures on the wall were all by Lodge or Thorburn, and most of them depicted partridges bursting over a high thorn fence in the instant before their dissolution, or grouse and pheasants as seen by the eye of their slayer in that perilous instant when they were about to cross the line of guns. Here was a brace of teal, braking down incautiously to their deaths on the edge of a Norfolk broad, and here, strangely enough, was a very good picture of a stag; (for George Proteron did not stalk, a practice which he had once contemptuously described as "pottering about on one's stomach after sitters"). He was a noble beast though, as he stood there in the frame, his head turned towards the painter, every fibre of him defiantly alive, in the moment that someone would probably remember for thirty years, when the stag himself was nothing but a pair of antlers on a wall.

Yes, thought Charles, we are a queer nation, half devil and half child. As a classical scholar, brought up on Kipling and the Church of England, Charles had only the vaguest ideas about what happened in the after-life. But he felt that George Proteron, wherever he went, would contrive to be a nuisance if his club-form was any criterion. *He* would never settle down to harping or whatever one did. Charles could imagine him planning a hate down below against the old cocks, or worrying St. Peter to get his asphodel-burning accomplished in good time.

But perhaps these speculations were premature: the old boy was not dead yet and, even now when he lay unconscious, it was somehow impossible to imagine him with all his ferocity stilled for ever and the village choir at Five Mile Wallop singing over him:

"For all the Saints who from their labours rest."

Still the doctor did not come, and Charles could not resist drawing out one of the red shooting-journals and turning its pages. The tabulated figures of slaughtered game, each after its kind, appalled him. Had all these living things gone, year by year, simply to be the *raison-d'être* of this old anachronism, just to make George Proteron a Roman holiday? The comments opposite each day's figures were terse and stereotyped:

"A fine day, wind SSW. Had 4 fair drives before luncheon from the Mendlesham side and one very pretty one off the heath afterwards when we got 41 brace, mostly Frenchmen. I shot well for me, getting 151 in 187 car."

Or :

"A poor day spoilt by fog. Birds very low and slow and a lot went wrong. We only had 53 brace up to luncheon. H.R.H. in good form: I wiped his eye twice at the Long Belt but of course pretended it was a mistake. Own gun 72 par, 4 hares."

And again:

"A red-letter day on the Haricot beat. Birds came beautifully and on the wind were worth a lot of money. 400 brace is the previous record for the moor and there should be a big pick-up."

And that, thought Charles, means the poor birds he and his friends tinkered or nearly missed, probably after luncheon. Cold-blooded old brute! to Charles a grouse was a grouse, a glorious quarry to be dreamed

31

of, to be sought eagerly on foot over leagues of heather, to be gloated over if he was lucky enough to bring it down, to be carried home and eaten in triumph. To George Proteron it was just another dot in his endless bowling analysis, the nicely calculated less or more.

His grouse and his drinks: when each had been downed, each was forgotten, but at least he did number the former in his game-journal. Charles' mind suddenly wondered what George Proteron's liquor-journal would look like with no close-season and seven days a week. But at that moment the doctor bustled in with Martin Kenyon and the young man fled from the Club.

VII

HEATHER-BED

Mournful from things defeated in the throes
Of memory of some conquered hunting-ground,
Where no life came except defeated life . . . . .

George Proteron awoke in a raging draught and with some small hard object scratching the side of his head. He moved a little and wondered dully at the soft downy feeling of something round his neck. Had he got his fur coat on? Then with a start he realized that he was crouching on his face.

What the deuce could have happened? He could not be in bed, for both he and Alfred Leicester knew that fresh air, especially at night, belonged most definitely out of doors and it was as much as Alfred's job was worth to admit it after sundown. Worse still, George vaguely felt as if he had been out all night for his nose was damp and the draught seemed quite intolerable. He squinted down the bridge of his nose and could see what must be dew-drops marshalled along it.

Good God! he had not been left out at night since that frightful party, forty-two years ago, when Pongo Fergusson had celebrated his coming-of-age in Naini Tal. Pongo Fergusson had been a pretty hard case even for the old 70th, and he had effectually stunned most of his surviving guests long after midnight by mixing the Widow with Water-

loo brandy and offering it to them in beer mugs. So much so that George and two other subalterns, still in mess-kit and tartan trews, had been found sleeping peacefully at 9 a.m. next day under a rose-bush in the Financial Commissioner's garden. And then they had only been awakened by a *mali* who was intent on watering the bush.

But that was forty-two years ago. What the this and that had happened now? George turned softly on his side and stretched out a leg to see if by any chance he had gone to bed with his boots on.

The shock was appalling. Instead of a well-arched instep or a neat patent-leather boot, George found himself gazing at three slender scutellated toes covered with gray-dark feathering down to the black and horny nails in which they ended. He rolled a horror-stricken eye upwards and around him: he could see nothing but a rim of heather-twigs—one of which had been scratching his neck—against a background above and on every side of gray and cloudy sky.

Suddenly George knew everything. He drew in those loathsome dark claws and sat on them, shivering, for many minutes as the ghastly truth swept over him. He, the Honourable George Hysteron-Proteron, sometime Commanding the Loyal Highlanders, a Gentleman of the King's Bodyguard of Scottish Archers, a Member of Boodle's, a Committee Member of the Qu'hais' Club, a Companion of the Bath, and a Justice of the Peace in and for Cambridgeshire, Lord of the Manor of Five Mile Wallop, and brother of the third Baron Parable of Achna-

garry, had been somehow metamorphosed into what he had so often described to others as "the best bird that flies".

He was, in other words, a grouse, no more and no less.

It was many minutes before poor George could move, and then he raised himself to his full height of nine and a half inches and peered hopelessly and helplessly over the rim of the heather which once he had trodden so lightly gun in hand, and about which he had been wont for so many years to rhapsodize to his cronies in the club. It seemed to stretch all round him for miles, dark and monotonous, without a house or a civilized object to break its everlasting sameness, its savagery and loneliness. George had often boasted that he had shot on all the best moors on both sides of the Border for the best part of forty years, but he had known them only from 9 a.m. to 5 p.m., as it were, in the early autumn. To wake up suddenly, covered with dew and on a very empty stomach, in the middle of an unknown moor which was probably swarming with vermin, was altogether too much for him.

And not only nature, but man must be against him now. . . . "Alfre—ed!" he tried to shout despairingly, and again: "Alfre—ed!" but even that old solace was denied him. The cry trailed down the wind as a curious grating chuckle which sounded like "Go—back—g'back—back!" George realized at once, and for the first time, the meaning of the word "to grouse". It meant to have an overwhelming grievance against fate, with only two inadequate words to vent it. From now on, it would be his lot to chuckle angrily at men and flee from them impotently, launching himself, without map-references, from place to place of this vast desert of heather and hill.

George turned at last and ran feverishly down a tiny path in the heather which led from the depression where he had awakened. He pattered on and on, stumbling over heather-stems with the dew-drops soaking his flanks, until at last he came to an open space where a burn ran between banks of gritty peat. Not thus had George been wont to quench his thirst on mornings when the outlook had seemed similarly bleak. But now he was fain to drink from the brown stream and lifted his head gratefully as the cool water trickled down his throat. He could have done, he felt, with a devilled bone very nicely, but this time sheer hunger made him pluck at some heather-stems beside him. It was a foul and insipid diet, and George was tempted to add a few morsels of quartz grit to it: at all events they would help to irritate his aching stomach as a thousand devilled bones had done of yore.

His pangs stayed at last, George crouched again to think. He had no idea where he was, but from the look of the heather and the signs of careful burning and draining, he guessed this must be a keepered moor: which meant that there was a man somewhere, not too far away, whose duty it was to guard and look after George. But George realized that the metamorphosis had deprived him of articulate speech, though not of thought. He had only those two infernal words "Go back!" left in his vocabulary, and if he flew up to a keeper's cottage and attempted to explain, the dunderhead would probably think he was a diseased bird and make haste to "put him down". Old cocks, as George knew, if alone, were regarded as vermin all the year round on all the best moors.

Similarly, it was no good flying south and appealing to any of his old cronies at the Club or to Alfred Leicester. Apart from the scarcity of heather in London, George felt sure that he would speedily encounter some thoughtless oaf, and a few hours later there would be a paragraph in the evening papers that "a red grouse in an exhausted condition had been picked up in Ryder Street, St. James's, and was now in the Natural History Museum."

That would be George's epitaph; and some pundit would write next day explaining to the public that he must have been driven south from Derbyshire during a recent gale. And one of George's club-mates would write to the *Squire*, pointing out solemnly that this was the fifth occurrence of *Lagopus scoticus* in the Home Counties since 1831, and adding some drivel about grouse-migration, based on certain half-baked observations he had once heard at luncheon during a very bad season in Renfrewshire. And poor George would lie entombed for ever in a drawer in the Birdroom in Cromwell Road, with his inside stuffed with tow and his legs neatly tied together with a label on them.

No, for better or worse, George would have to continue a grouse for the rest of his life. It would never do to give oneself up voluntarily to these callous, treacherous, thoughtless brutes to whom George was "one of the best birds that fly".

At that very moment, when George was finally resigned to the crushing blow fate had dealt him, there was a whirr above his head which made him duck involuntarily, and then he saw a big pack of grouse vanishing over the curve of the moor. George had only once flown before, and that was to Paris on a stormy November day, when he had been quite content to leave the technical side to the pilot and concentrate on not being sick. But now his loneliness was such that, without more ado, he found himself scurrying feverishly in his feather gaiters across the grass by the burn and launching himself into the wind as if he had been flying all his life.

A moment later and barely three feet from the ground, George had banked and was hurtling at forty miles an hour after the pack which were now dark specks three or four hundred yards in front of him. He tried to call out to them to stop, but no words came except that curious whirring chuckle. He raised and lowered each wing in turn to get the feel of the air-currents and stop the wind from getting under his feathers; then skimmed on with his eyes on where the pack had disappeared. A minute later he came to a little ridge and could see no sign of them. Then he realized that they had turned up into the wind and settled in a flat stretch of short young heather in front of him.

George skimmed eagerly towards them. He had no knowledge of landing-speed or alighting into the wind, so made a rather flustered crash-landing with his head down which nearly ended in a somersault. He was picking himself up and straightening his feathers and trying to look dignified, when an old grouse ran at him furiously, bristling with menace from crown to toe.

"Brr—*back*! go back, go back, back!" he chuckled. "What the devil are you doing in my Pack, sir?"

On his day, George Proteron had stood no nonsense from anyone, but this was not his day. He was so lonely and so relieved at knowing what was said to him that he made no attempt to show fight. To his delight he found that to another grouse he could make himself understood.

"Very sorry, I'm sure! Just up here on a visit and rather lost m' way," he muttered; then, force of old habit reasserting itself: "M' own club closed this month for redecorating. Member of Boodle's: perhaps . . . er . . . permit temporary membership here?"

The moment he said it, it sounded absurd. Who in Scotland had ever heard of Boodle's? The excuses died away in a mumble. Luckily the old cock-grouse accepted them.

"That's all right, old cock," he said heartily; "must keep an eye on strangers, and some of my young hens are very forward this season. Takes me all my time to look after them. You from Boodle's, eh? Good season there so far?"

He spoke as though Boodle's were a grouse-moor. Then he settled down side by side with George and fluffed out his feathers to dust in a tiny open patch of sand. George shuffled and squatted and tried to copy him.

"Oh, quite a good year, thanks," said George absently. He could not

37

help thinking how extraordinarily this old bird resembled one Euan Begbie of the Glasgow Light Infantry, with whom, before he died, George had soldiered and argued and shot for more years than he cared to count. He had been mad on training, and had even tried to institute a course for beaters and flankers in Morayshire one year, before the season opened.

At that moment a gaunt old grouse with the skin showing through the feathers of her scrawny neck ran up towards them, clucking under her breath.

"Hullo, Lizzie!" said the Begbie-bird. "Anything the matter?"

"Aye," said Lizzie, "I was just coming over to tak' this bird's name and number, Sirr, for loiterrin'." She spoke in a strange Border dialect and glared at George fiercely. "He came in a fu' minute after we did! Dae ye not ken that the Bogle-hawk'll get ye if ye're idlin'? It's the fat auld anes and the daft young anes that the Bogle-hawk feeds on! Dinna glower at me now!"

George had not been rated by a woman for twenty-five years. He had not been threatened with any bogey, man or bird, since he was three. He drew himself up and looked down his mandibles at Lizzie.

"My good woman," he began . . .

Aunt Lizzie, as he was to know her later, detonated furiously.

"There's nae my guid wumman aboot it," she cackled, "ye'll obey my orrders, auld cock or nae, or ye'll awa' to the march and may the foxes and the thread-wurrum get ye! I'll hae nae mutineers in this pack. I'll leave him tae ye, Sir Euan."

And she whirred away, clucking.

George tried to laugh it off. A few days back, if anyone had dared to speak to him like that, he or she would have been up before the committee or never asked out by him again. One thought a lot about people in club-life, but the thoughts were rarely voiced.

"Lizzie's quite right, y'know," said the Begbie-bird, half apologetically, shuffling on to his side and dropping a lid over one hazel eye. "It's the stragglers and the slow ones that get hurt. This has been a wonderful year so far and I've got down very seriously to training. I've finished my covey-training and we're trying to get a fortnight or so of pack-exercises. It's a bumper year, worse luck!"

"What?" exclaimed George involuntarily. He had never yet heard anyone regretting that it was a bumper year for grouse.

"Well, up here it's been a most extraordinary season so far: a very good stock, no late snow to spoil the hatch, no disease and the heather better than I've ever known it. Perhaps you'd care to muck in with us. I'm O.C. Pack, y'know, and I can't afford to take risks. Otherwise those great bastards from the South will be taking advantage of us!"

So in the next few days George, the new grouse, learnt much and painfully. Aunt Lizzie did not put him, as he feared, "on the square", but she insisted on the Pack-orders being minutely obeyed, and George was soon stiff and sore with practice alarms, with running out up-wind when a shepherd appeared on the skyline and with the effort of keeping up with the Pack in their lightning manœuvres when they turned across the wind or rose suddenly a hundred feet in the air. Aunt Lizzie taught him to squat like a hunted hare while men walked thirty yards away, and to fly towards, and not away from, any man who did not carry a gun. She insisted on his not eating too much, and stopped him from trying to sleep in some wind-sheltered cranny where a fox or a marten might get him unawares. There were always three or four old birds standing rigid and erect with both eyes open for men or eagles or peregrine falcons, what time the rest of the Pack were comfortably feeding or dozing, or dusting on the gritty road which cut the moor.

George, as a result of his earlier *gaffe*, found himself detailed far too frequently for this fatigue. He was too busy by day and too tired by night to worry overmuch about the monstrous blow fate had landed him, but he did realize that, in speaking of the life of the "finest bird that flies", it all depended on one's point of view.

Aunt Lizzie, he found, was a fourth-season hen who had been blown up from the Borders in the "Muckle Gale" of 1935. In that season she had sustained a non-vital wound which had precluded all hopes of offspring, and had thus become a sort of great-aunt as well as sergeant-major to the coveys in Sir Euan's pack. She was never tired of repeating that she had been "ower the tap" at least a dozen times, and with her Border speech and manners had achieved a great local reputation among her politer Highland neighbours. Her tales lost nothing in the telling and half an hour with Aunt Lizzie as the coveys gathered to jug in the chill twilight and the wind whistled over the darkling heather, reminded George Proteron of Grimm's fairy tales which had been out of his mind for sixty years. There were, with Aunt Lizzie, no witches or dragons or wolves indeed, but red-faced pop-eyed bogles, as she

39

called them, who lurked in little round holes in the heather and spat fire with terrifying sounds if one flew near them.

Only on the third evening did George realize that he himself must be not only a legend in eastern Scotland, but one of the Master-Bogles of them all. He crouched down to roost shivering with a fear of the unknown.

VIII

THE EARL'S BUTT

George woke stiff and sore on the fourth morning, and was almost a defaulter as the Pack whirred away through the mist to its feeding-ground. Aunt Lizzie always chose one as far as possible from where they had spent the night, in case some falcon had marked them on the previous evening. They settled in some broken ground on the crest of a rise and George, endeavouring to stay his hunger, wondered for the twentieth time how the Picts had ever managed to brew any stimulant such as heather-ale. At last, wet with dew, he joined two young cocks who were on sentry-go on a little bank of peat which rose a foot or so above the damp heather.

As the mists smoked off the moor in the early sunlight, George, preening hard, found himself gazing across leagues of purple heather towards a nick in a ridge which somehow seemed familiar. Surely he had seen it before? Then gazing down his back-feathers, as he sifted and combed his dripping primaries, he realized with a shock that the peat-bank on which he was sitting was the rim of a grouse-butt: here was one of the caverns of those very Bogles of whom Aunt Lizzie had told the Pack such a breathless fairy-tale the night before.

It was a circular butt, well-sunk, well-drained, well-built of stones and peat, with a timbered floor and an entrance at the side. George in his day had stood in a thousand such, but what galvanized his horrified attention was a small granite plaque let into the peat-sods beside the entrance.

Good Godfathers! no wonder he recognized this bit of moor! He

40

knew, without reading them, the words which were engraved on that stone: "THE EARL'S BUTT. 14. 8. 1919."

It was, it could be, none other than the historic butt in which James Lumphanan, the last and most eccentric of the Earls of Glencairn, had crowned his remarkable career by a deed which even now was spoken of with bated breath wherever grouse-shooters were wont to congregate. On that August morning between 10 and 10.30 a.m. James Glencairn had made £6,000, by telephone, on the Liverpool cotton-market, had proposed marriage to the celebrated Miss Nina Waddilove of the Jollity Theatre, and in the selfsame butt had shot forty-seven grouse in exactly fifty-one cartridges, using a single gun. It was a record which so far stood quite by itself.

George could see the little ledge on which in those days the "laird's telephone" had been installed. For it was his lordship's invariable habit to occupy the most likely butt on his own moors and to put his guests, usually in order of social precedence, to right or left of him. In each of the butts most favoured by the Earl, a portable telephone had always been installed by means of which he could commune, during the duller earlier moments of the drive, with his stockbroker, or his bookmaker, or some other of those whom he was pleased to call his "auxiliaries".

The Earl of Glencairn was only a memory now in Aberdeenshire, but on that far-off morning George himself and Alfred Leicester had occupied the next butt downwind, and had been unable to avoid over-hearing certain passages in his whirlwind courtship of Miss Waddilove. George had sworn later, at the breach of promise trial, on his oath and on his reputation, that no shooting man on earth could possibly either have obtained such a bag while making a serious proposal of marriage to a woman, or could have found time to propose while making it. And as the bag was not in dispute, the inference had been that the proposal was all Miss Waddilove's eye and had never taken place. Lord Glencairn himself, in cross-examination, had conceded that he might have done it by mistake when his mind was engrossed with the oncoming birds. He had repudiated any suggestion that he had done it for a bet. But a special jury, composed, as George remembered, of frightful fellows, none of whom had ever been on a grouse-moor in their lives, had decided that the whole affair indicated an abnormal degree of callousness. They had assessed the damages accordingly. Poor Jimmie Glencairn had hinted later to George that that drive had cost him well over a monkey despite his deal on the market.

But George found small comfort in recalling these by-gone battles now. Here was he, a grouse, perched on the most notorious butt in the middle of one of the best-known moors in Scotland, and one moreover to which he had actually been invited for the Twelfth by old General Blount-Garamie, the present owner. George's marksmanship made him welcome all over the Kingdom, and since James Glencairn's day he had often been an honoured guest at Banchovie Lodge. With a shudder he now realized that this year, unless he was careful, he was unlikely to arouse any comment there at all except as a runner or on the *menu*.

By now the August morning was hot on the heather and George found Aunt Lizzie beside him on the rim of the butt. She was straining her scrawny neck, which always looked as if it had been plucked, for possible enemies and watching with her sergeant-major's eye for any signs of indiscipline in the Pack sunning and dusting themselves around them.

George's eye caught hers.

"Aye, George," she said quietly. "This is yin of they Bogle's hidey-holes I was tellin' ye of! They're awa' the noo, the muckle sons of shame, but no when the war's declared!"

"But when *is* war declared?"

George had realized that it was not a bit of good asking what the date was, or talking about the Twelfth to this clucking old maid who had never been anything but a grouse.

"How would we ken? The traitorous beasties! Ae day ye'll wauken and a's well and it's peace on a' the moor. The next ye'll wauken and it's war, wi' red flags loupin' ower the brae and a wheen beasties yowlin' awa' to frichten a' before them. But *they're* no the beasties ye need fear! It's the red-faced pop-eyed bogles that gang bump in their hidey-holes, and the next ye ken they've dragged ye ben the heather and eaten ye. . . . Losh! yon's three great beasties coming the noo. Doon we flit and awa' with us all!"

She scuttered down off the rim of the butt and ran clucking in a half-circle to rouse the Pack. She and Sir Euan commenced to herd it quietly up the hill into deeper heather.

A sudden idea struck George. He stood on the butt whence all but he had fled and looked down towards the advancing figures. There were

42

two tall men with a black spaniel, and they had turned off the path and were moving up the line of butts. When they were two hundred yards away, Aunt Lizzie came racing back furiously to George. Her eyes gleamed as red as any cock-bird's.

"Did ye no' hear me?" she chuckled. "Ye'll be for orrders the noo, ye loiterrer!"

But for once George stood his ground.

"Sorry, tactical reconnaissance . . . must stay . . . no danger . . . enemy intentions . . . see you on the Black Strath later!"

He ducked into the heather as Aunt Lizzie ran furiously away.

George crouched and crept some forty yards and then drew himself up stiffly beside the next butt, his head just above the heather. He knew of old, Norman Garamie's spaniel, Heather, a chuckle-headed cocker bitch whose indifferent nose was always being belied by the never-ceasing movements of her feathered behind. The wind was right and unless she got too near, he might overhear what those two were saying.

They strode up the hill, and George soon saw that the taller one was Sir Norman Blount-Garamie himself, "old N.B.G." as he had been known by the troops ever since that historic morning when he had suddenly remembered it was a Sunday and postponed his newly-launched offensive until a more appropriate day. A regular soldier and a very keen sportsman, General Garamie had shot almost everything in India and Africa and Europe, except perhaps man. This last omission had been, of course, entirely due to his successive posts on the Staff. The other, a lanky figure with a cheerful, red, bony face, was Michael Arbuckle, once an equerry to a Royal Duke and afterwards joint-master of the Blankman. Both, George knew, if not in the very first flight, were by no means contemptible shots.

"Is this the first time you've shot here?" the General asked, as the two paused and lit pipes in the shelter of the Earl's Butt.

"Oh Lord, no! Old Jimmie Glencairn was a sort of uncle of mine, and he used to ask me up here occasionally when I was a boy and put me in an outside butt all day. I remember the how-de-do there was over *this* butt!"

"Ah! now tell me, Michael, did he leave much when he died?"

"Damn all, one way and another. He was rather fond of me, but all I inherited were his fishing rods, his library, i.e., three bound volumes

43

of the *Winning Post,* and a hundred-acre farm in the middle of our Friday country, which was wired up like a ruddy canary's cage. It cost me about five pounds an acre to make it rideable." He laughed. "Do you still drive this moor the way Jimmie did?"

"Yes, very nearly, though our bags have gone up a lot. We start with these butts, taking it both ways and bringing in all those little corries by the march. The birds are bound to come right, for this bit is a natural wind-trap and they've nowhere else to go."

George ground his mandibles as he listened. Oh, hadn't they? Not if he and Aunt Lizzie knew it.

The General went on. "Then we ought to get a very pretty drive over there on what we call the Black Strath. I've moved the whole line of butts into that gully which you can just see. One has to shoot dam' quick, I grant you, but the butts can't be seen and, after all, Michael, it's the drives where you *have* to be quick which are the killing ones. And we'll get all the old cocks there which try to sneak out on the down-wind side, as well as one or two big lots we never got on terms with last year."

Aunt Lizzie that must have been, thank goodness for her! George's heart glowed for a second. He had been shivering, for all his feathers, at these calm butcher-like proposals. Then his blood ran cold again.

"I'm not going to draw for places at that drive, Michael. I've got an excellent team, but I'm going to put my three very strongest guns on the down-wind side. I wish old George Proteron hadn't failed me! *He'd* have dealt with the beggars!"

Michael Arbuckle's voice, slangy and drawling, put in:

"Where *is* old George P. then? I must confess I never had much time for him, especially after the years I spent with the Blankman under his brother Bill. But everyone in town is being most mysterious about him. Has he by any chance run off with someone in his old age? I wouldn't put it past him, especially as I heard he'd actually invited that young American wench, Madeleine Cranmer, into his butt last year at Tomintoul. Old George must be breaking up, or is he really nesting?"

George had now no teeth to gnash, but he ground his mandibles as he squatted impotently in the heather and listened to these outrageous aspersions on his past. He realized again what "grousing" meant: it meant to have a champion grievance with no power on earth to hit back.

"Nesting?" chuckled General Garamie; "oh, good heavens, no! He passed out in the Club smoking-room after lunch about ten days ago, and is in a nursing home at the moment. Sammy Glemham tells me it's very doubtful if he'll ever pull a trigger again. Of course," the deprecating damnatory voice went on, "he'd always done himself *remarkably* well. Everyone wondered how he shot as beautifully as he did. As Sammy Glemham said to me, if old George never has another drop, he'll have had his whack! But even without him, I've got a very adequate team: Sammy's coming and Mark Puddick, and *they'll* keep the bag up; and Nigel, of course yes; and Crasher Casserole is a really *useful* shot and on his day brilliant, if nothing has happened to upset him."

He paused and knocked out his pipe.

"As you know, Michael, it's Sunday and I never bet in any case, but if we don't get 300 brace here on Tuesday, and about the same on the other beat next day, I shall be *most* disappointed. Dugald MacLeish and Ian and all my fellows are burning to beat the record for the moor. Heather, you bitch, come *bike*!"

But George had heard quite enough. Was he to cower there and listen to these snake-blooded beings making arrangements for his slaughter? Was he to offer himself on Tuesday as a mark to Crasher Casserole, his lifelong rival, whom he himself had taught to shoot years ago, and who, on his day, was one of the most jealous and deadly shots in the Kingdom? Crasher would shoot a bird off the muzzle of some-

one else's gun. Crasher had . . . but he still remembered that disgrace-
ful affair of the woodcock at Campsey. Crasher was . . . but he supposed they all were. To this crowd of sadists, if he fell on Tuesday on
the stricken field, he would not be Colonel the Honourable George
Hysteron-Proteron, C.B., J.P., dead on the field of honour, but just
half a brace of grouse, and a tough one at that, mere Purdey-fodder,
lost in a record bag.

Heather-the-Bitch was still snuffling and feathering twenty yards
away from him across the wind, and by her stern suggesting that she
expected to flush the Loch Ness monster at any moment. But George
swung himself into the air and, with what he hoped was a defiant
chuckle, swept away down the wind. To his hearers he was just another
old cock who commanded neither a covey nor a pack, and was there-
fore barren and would be better out of the way. . . . But Scotland in
August is full of amateur naturalists.

George skimmed low across the moor, turning and sidling ever so
little to keep the wind from getting under his feathers, and stalled at
last in the middle of the Black Strath to find the Pack all round him.

Aunt Lizzie ånd Euan came running anxiously towards him.

"Well, what news?"

"Plenty," gulped George. "I want all your covey commanders
urgently. . . . Got the enemy's general and special ideas . . . vital in-
formation . . . essential to act quickly!" George's mind was still groping
back to the staff-rides of his youth. It was eighteen years since he had

done any soldiering, and much more than that since he had done any in terror of his life. "Get 'em together quickly.

Z day is the day after tomorrow. We must have a try-out tomorrow."

As the Pack gathered round him eagerly, George lifted up his voice and spoke.

IX

TEAM-WORK

Two nights later George jugged down on the edge of the Pack, stiff and sore from his crown to his claws and as wing-weary as any grouse could well be. He did not know how many hundred miles Aunt Lizzie and he had flown (to poor George it seemed like thousands), or how many hundred grouse had listened to his urgent warning, on that beat or the next. But they had all received it. For the first time in history, the occupants of a grouse-moor were ready for what was going to happen on the Twelfth.

It had not been an easy task at all. He had had first to convince Aunt Lizzie and Sir Euan of what he knew, without giving himself away. He had then to warn all the other grouse which in packs and coveys and twos and threes were scattered over six or seven thousand acres of heather. There were the old cocks who, not unnaturally, resented any attempt to interfere with their packs, and were as fiercely conservative over flight routes and feeding areas and the "custom of the moor" as any of George's cronies in the Qu'hais' smoking-room. There were head-strong young coveys, glorying in their powers of flight, disdainful of their anxious parents, and most of whom had never seen a shot fired; to these George appeared to be just an old cock with "the wind under his tail". There were the conventionalists who had always flown that way because the lie of the ground or the set of the wind seemed to make "that way" inevitable; and there were the ordinary grouse, hundreds of them, who had never heard of Aunt Lizzie and her bogey-eagles and flew, as a matter of course, away from any human being who showed a flag.

But George felt that somehow they had "put his message over" to their hearers, as the two sped like a fiery cross from place to place about the Banchovie moorland. It was not the least of his woes that he found it impossible to tell his successive audiences how he came by his knowledge. That would have involved George saying what he had once been, like an evangelist who declaims what a terrible sinner he was of yore until he saw the light. And George, never yet a martyr to any cause, had no intention of being torn limb from limb by angry grouse. Luckily, he had little time to think out what effects his crusade would have on the history of shooting. He was just George, the grouse-bird with a message.

So now as the August dusk fell, he snuggled himself into his feather collar and spread out his downy bosom to keep his toes warm as he and Aunt Lizzie crouched beak to breeze on the outskirts of the Pack. His thoughts roved back over the last fifty seasons, each one of which he had been wont to commence in his game-journal with the phrase:

"Here beginneth my .... season, age ...., weight .... A lovely day with a strong .... wind. Birds very forward. . . ."

and so on. He knew exactly what was happening in London. The morning papers, especially *The Times*, would all be carrying special articles on the Twelfth, and the cheaper ones would inevitably prefix the word "glorious" or refer somehow to the "Feast of Saint Grouse". There would be portraits (there had been of George in years gone by) of great ones "in the butts" in the very act of slaughter. In the evening papers next day someone would be sure to write that "on all the principal moors sportsmen were early astir" (though George himself in other years had always firmly declined to be astir before 7.15). And some oaf, who probably hailed from Whitechapel, was bound to commit a *gaffe* about the "crack of the rifle" being heard on the moors. Poulterers in Leadenhall and Jermyn Street and in the vaults of the Savoy had already, George felt certain, blast them! the hundreds of brace of young grouse hanging on hooks which officially would be shot and "flown to London" next day in time to grace the luncheon of despicable stockbrokers and attorneys and others whom no one had ever asked to shoot. And in lodge after lodge, from Derbyshire to Caithness, parties of expectant grouse-shooters, male and, bless George's soul, even female nowadays, were dining, conscious that tomorrow they would participate, solemnly and enjoyably, in one of the main social events of a gentleman's year.

48

No one in all that crowd, George knew, would spare that night so much as one thought of pity for the legions of doomed birds sleeping so austerely over fifty thousand square miles of heather; they had done man no wrong, but tomorrow they must die simply because they were grouse, exciting to shoot at and good to eat. Against them war had been declared long ago by Act of Parliament, but they alone would know it not till their doom was upon them.

George shivered a little, then tucked his head in his back-feathers and fell asleep, too tired to worry any more.

In the lodge at Banchovie that evening all was peace. His "team", as General Garamie liked to call them, had dined excellently but not too heavily on salmon and a roast of lamb; the port decanter had only been round once ("just to drink the King"), for it was an oft-repeated saying of the General's that "to shoot really well a man ought to be as fit as if he had to fight for his life". He himself had never actually had to do so, but he always picked his guns very carefully and self-indulgence was frowned on. George alone, of all his regular guests, had been a law unto himself, and only George's exceptional brilliance as a shot, and his ownership of Five Mile Wallop, had kept him still on the General's list.

The party all knew each other well and had by now exchanged most of their grouse-shooting shop at dinner: "Poor Gerald, yes, he's had a most indifferent hatch, a lot of eggs frozen, and the heather beetle's been worrying him since . . . Let me see, who *has* got Morven this year, oh yes, some Americans at a quite staggering figure, considering the stock Tom left there. . . . Yes, we had quite a pretty little week at Crashie last September, not a petticoat in the lodge. . . . Fourth time over, but they always seem to have birds there . . . are you? I'm going to the Duke on the 19th . . . oh, average year only, he tells me . . . poor old Snooper, he was always a bit of a boy-scout at m'tutor's, but now he's gone all romantic and taken a dogging moor in Kintyre . . . Jimmy Smitherman told me it's the sort of place where you walk twenty-five miles a day for 2½ brace . . . a very fair little hatch, he assures me, and he's taken on the Dalziel beat from The MacMurtrie, which rounds him off very nicely. . . . *Strongylosis* my foot! it's his keeper! He *will* not burn and he doesn't know the first thing about a moor!"

Thus and thus did they talk, as self-centred and unintelligible as Hughli pilots.

And now in the long chairs of the smoking-room they lay on their spines and savoured their coffee and pipes, all except Heather-the-bitch, who had flattened herself out on the hearthrug, her legs behind her and spread out sideways as if she had been spatch-cocked. Gradually the deep content of well-ordered certainty settled on the room. Michael Arbuckle rose and went to a writing-table, and soon became busy with a hound-list and a most illiterate scrawl his huntsman had sent him after the first day's cubbing. General Garamie, in his chair by the fire, checked and rechecked his meticulous arrangements for the morrow: map, horn, whistle, extractor, guns, cartridges, drives, beaters, flankers, loaders, dogs, luncheon, drinks, ice, game-labels and trains; for to him a day's grouse-driving needed from start to finish the most careful "operation orders". Presently Lord Charles Casserole and Colonel Puddick rose and settled down to a silent and scientific game of bridge with Lord Glemham and Nigel Blount-Garamie, the General's nephew.

There was, in fact, only one discordant note in the room, and that was the presence of a long-haired, sharp-featured, palely grubby young man in a silk shirt and a double-breasted dinner-coat; he wore mauve socks and was reading a volume of poems on a sofa, seemingly unaware of the harsh glances occasionally bestowed on him. This was none other than Rupert Pilimore, George Proteron's nephew, whom we last met in a police cell on the Kingston By-pass. Rupert earned a precarious livelihood on the fringe of the stage and journalism: sometimes he decorated the houses of his more eccentric friends in the latest mode, sometimes he photographed or paragraphed important social events and personages for the weekly newspapers.

That was how he came to be, so incongruously, at Banchovie. Sir Norman had never despised publicity when it came his way, and he hoped in a few days' time to see a half-page of photographs in *Sport and the Stage* with the familiar caption: "The Twelfth. General Sir Norman Blount-Garamie, K.C.M.G., and party at Banchovie Lodge, Aberdeenshire. From left to right . . . (inset right) The party on the way to the moors. (Below left) Sir Norman takes a high one."

But he was just beginning to realize the truth of the saying " *souffrir pour être belle*". He had introduced Rupert to all and sundry as "poor George Proteron's nephew" and an added glamour had hung about the youth by reason of his recent arrest and conviction. But the

General was not prepared for someone who dared to talk at dinner about Chaliapin and *décor* and sex-urge, and whose one adjective seemed to be "too devastating". However, the menacing crackle of the other guests' shirt-fronts and the gleam of their polished and rosy skulls had gradually silenced Rupert and, after a few feeble twitterings, he had vanished into the hall before the port to commune audibly down a hundred miles of wire with someone in Forfarshire whom he

51

called "Madeleine darling" at every sentence, and who clearly had no sense of time or shame or gentlemen's meal-times. Sir Norman by now could not help wondering how George Proteron could possibly be related, either by blood or tears, to this unspeakable young man.

On the north side of the house, Dugald MacLeish, the head-keeper, knocked out his pipe and, after a final circular glance at the weather, turned to go upstairs to bed. His wife had been, as usual, cooking in the Lodge and would not be up for an hour or more, for she had to keep an

eye on the two middle-aged house-maids, lest they forgot themselves among so many smart south-country loaders. (The latter, however, seemed to prefer whisky-poker to dalliance, and had so far said nothing to shock Mrs. MacLeish's sensitive Highland ears.) Dugald though, like all game-keepers, a professional pessimist, was for once in a reasonably satisfied frame of mind. He had walked twenty miles that day, putting last-minute touches to the butts and staking out the exact positions he wanted certain flankers and pointsmen to occupy. His guns, all of whom he knew well by sight or reputation, were most unlikely to let him down, and he had just the beaters he wanted. Only Dugald knew there were more grouse on the moor than there had been in the last seventeen seasons, and nothing but a westerly gale or a wandering eagle could make much difference to tomorrow's bag.

As he slipped into his long flannel night-shirt and snuffed the candle with his horny finger and thumb, Dugald's mind held only two cares: the evening train left Kirkintoul at seven, and he might have a job on the morrow to get his grouse packed and labelled in time to catch the train; and the "young bitch", who had all her mother's nose

and steadiness, and was the dead spit of her on a line, was just a wee thing inclined to pinch her birds when she picked them.

Dugald thrashed his long limbs in the sheets for a moment and then slept: in his dreams he could see a line of red and white flags, and before them dark dots and lines and clusters of birds streaming endlessly to the hidden butts as he had always willed them to do.

Only Dinah, the young bitch, stirred uneasily in her straw. Dugald, true to his custom, had given all his dogs half-rations that evening to make them keener on the morrow; it might be a good scheme in some ways, but Dugald had unfortunately made no discrimination between mature women and growing girls.

X

REVOLT ON THE MOOR

The Twelfth that year at Banchovie has passed into legend. It was a lovely day with a light southerly breeze, though the early mist gave promise of heat to come. The beaters, trailing up the ridge to the first drive under Ian Murdoch, the under-keeper, said little. They had the best part of twenty-five miles to tramp before they reached their homes, and there would be plenty to talk about later on when they had seen a little more of "the Laird's" party in action and at lunchtime. From where they were walking, the curve of the hill hid the Banchovie beat below them, but they could look far over the northern beat, Glencairn, which was to be driven next day.

Grouse seemed to be everywhere. Coveys and small parties of two and three whirred continually off the ridge in front of them, and one great pack of nearly a hundred birds rose with a roar: they watched it settle a mile away by the burn.

"There's birds on the moor the day," said Allan Fraser, the policeman, appreciatively.

"Aye," said Ian, "it's no' been such a bad year, I'm hoping". He would not say more.

Two more big coveys skimmed away northwards in front of them. Old John Tye, Lord Glemham's keeper, who came up from Norfolk each year with a trio of young Labradors, gave a jerk at the thongs which held his panting charges and took the pipe from his mouth.

"There's wholly some birds here," he conceded, in his squeaky voice. "More'n ever I see in me life up here afore. Ah! that's a masterpiece, that is!"

The polite Highlanders felt that at last justice had been done them by a Sassenach. They lined out at the end of the drive and sat down in the heather to smoke and wait for the signal to move off.

Ten minutes later and nearly three miles away General Garamie's party reached the butts. There was no talking and no excitement: all were veterans who knew exactly what was expected of them. They

54

had drawn for places before leaving the lodge and were, as usual, moving two up after each drive. As each man reached his appointed butt, he settled himself on his shooting-seat with the barrels of his first gun resting on the edge of the butt. Each took a glance at the loader behind him with his great open bag of cartridges, shuffled his feet to make certain he could swing freely, and then swept his eyes round to each of the neighbouring butts, measuring expertly and instinctively the angles at which it was safe to shoot. Then they all settled down and appeared to doze in the sunshine, though actually their eyes and those of each loader were roving keenly over the moor; for they were a more or less professional team, and it was with nearly every man a point of honour not to be caught napping by any old cock or stray covey which might come over while the flankers were moving to their places.

General Garamie blew a long blast on a hunting-horn and a mile beyond on a ridge a flanker waved a red flag to start the unseen beaters far away. The General was thinking of the report he would have to send to his favourite journal that night. It would read something like this:

"BANCHOVIE. Six guns (General Sir Norman Blount-Garamie, K.C.M.G., Lord Glemham, Lord Charles Casserole, Colonel M. Puddick, D.S.O., Major M. Arbuckle, M.F.H., and Captain Nigel Blount-Garamie shot .... brace on the 12th. Weather fine with a light southerly breeze. Birds very forward and in some places packed. *No disease.*"

He hoped that the photographs already taken by "Twittering Rupert", as Michael Arbuckle had nicknamed the photographer, would turn out well. Rupert had distinguished himself, first by attempting to breakfast in bed, and then by appearing on the moor hatless in a gray lounge-suit, a pink shirt and a Balliol tie. He had since been put in charge of Nigel Garamie, with strict orders that he was to sit in the bottom of the butt and not to speak or move until the drive was over, on pain of being shot. Sir Norman

proposed to pose later on, in between the drives, for the photograph of himself in the act of taking a high one. Poor Rupert! he was crouching there now, biting his nails and feeling, as he remarked afterwards, like a gazelle in a herd of rhinoceros.

In the bottom butt, Lord Charles Casserole who, between ourselves, usually left the watching for the early birds to his loader, and was frankly bored by shooting unless birds were actually coming to him, drew a paper-backed novel from his pocket and read keenly on. It was one of those exciting stories in which at least five murders are committed and the pepperpot of suspicion is sprinkled liberally over the ten principal characters in turn. So far the only person in the story who was not under police surveillance, or who had not been black-jacked or chloroformed during the investigation, was the gray-eyed girl who seemed on the verge of reciprocating the young detective's passion. Could it possibly be Helen after all? Lord Charles hoped that the grouse would wait until he had finished Chapter XX.

In the butt above him Michael Arbuckle smoked a surreptitious cigarette and thought how much pleasanter this was than cantering

backwards and forwards in some steamy woodland, yodelling encouragement as his huntsman must be doing at the moment, and cursing under his breath at the heat, the horseflies and some excited child in pigtails who had just viewed her first fox.

Nigel Blount-Garamie, who took himself very seriously, had reduced Rupert to an almost tearful silence, and was now devoting a good deal of thought to the problem whether he could possibly work in two days at Lochquoyle between the Duke and the Grant-Menzies. He took out his well-worn engagement book and studied it long and earnestly, though his eyes never ceased to rove over the rim of the heather in front of him. Now that old George Proteron was *hors de combat*, he felt, there must be quite a number of hosts who would be looking out for a really adequate shot to fill his place and one who, unlike old George, always kept himself in the pink of condition.

Two miles away, on a rocky crag just outside the edge of the beat, George himself and Aunt Lizzie sat bolt upright side by side, straining their feathered ears. They had watched the beaters line out and start and disappear over the moor with their red and white flags waving. A prolonged silence followed.

"Well, well," said George, relaxing forty minutes later. "That's that!" He wondered what Napoleon had felt like in his prime or the Old Duke after Waterloo.

Aunt Lizzie fluffed all her feathers suddenly like a barndoor fowl and then scratched her scrawny neck with one hind toe.

"Aye," she muttered grimly. "We've beaten them the noo, the muckle sons of shame. Ye've done weel, George, and I'm no sayin' ye've not. We'll awa' and tell Sir Euan."

But it was probably sheer force of old habit which gave George a momentary tinge of regret, as he whirred down to Glencairn, a touch of pity for those poor misguided beasts, whose potent war-machine had for once in its history failed to function. Here were twenty-five beaters and flankers, two keepers and nine dogs, seven loaders and seven "guns", with a pony-boy and chauffeurs and what-not gathered so solemnly, after long months of careful mobilization, for what? A blitzkrieg on an empty moor. For once they had reckoned without their hosts.

XI

THE PRICE OF FAME

To say that Sir Norman Garamie and his head-keeper were bewildered, as the beaters closed in on the line of butts, is to put it very mildly indeed. Dugald, in fact, was almost in tears. Both knew well that a day or so previously this part of the moor had been alive with birds and that there was no question of disease. An eagle seemed equally unlikely. It was unthinkable that any miscreant had managed to put all the grouse off before the drive started. Yet . . . not once in twenty years had that drive proved blank! The guns changed places and faced about for the return drive with the feeling that, however badly they had started, they were on one of the best and most carefully-keepered moors in the Highlands and that another blank drive was impossible.

They were right. The drive contained one old cock-grouse, a recluse of long standing, who years before had been shell-shocked by a gun going off in his ear as he hurtled over the butts. He lived now a morose and self-centred existence, away from any covey, and all George's admonitions had failed to drive home to him the danger. Deaf though he was, he was as wary as he was tough. Flushed by the beaters a mile from the guns, he got up very high, and sixty yards before he reached the right-hand butt realized suddenly what lay before him. He did a lightning bank and turned down the line on the wind at seventy miles an hour. The salute that greeted his appearance reminded Colonel Puddick, who had just come up from Cowes, of a Royal review at Spithead. Almost everyone, it seemed, got off two barrels at him, and Crasher Casserole in No. 2 Butt, who had started shooting when the old cock was opposite No. 1 Butt and went on till he was over his left-hand neighbour, fired all four barrels. Sheer weight of metal, in fact, brought the gallant old warrior down at last, a strong runner and far out in front of the line. The day's sport had at any rate begun.

Far away on Glencairn George and Aunt Lizzie heard the fusillade. "Aye," said Aunt Lizzie, "I'm thinkin' that'll be Mactavish, the puir

deaf adder. That's what comes of stoppin' his ear. But perhaps he'll keep the bogles busy for a while. We're no' wanting them on Glencairn the day."

But in kindness to everyone, it is best to draw a veil over that morning. The bag up to luncheon consisted of one grouse, one golden plover and a hare, and no one's temper was improved by Rupert Pilimore's suggestion that the party should now pose for a group photograph with the bag laid out on the heather in front of them. After one more blank drive, Rupert felt, they might in their present mood start shooting him, so immediately luncheon was over, he made some excuse about "developing" and fled, unregretted, with his camera down the hillpath towards the lodge.

Dugald, who had been talking wildly to Ian Murdoch and old John Tye, came up after luncheon and implored the General to move over to the Glencairn beat where, in John Tye's Norfolk jargon, the grouse "fair swahmed". But this would have upset the General's established ritual: he had always for years shot the Banchovie beat on the Twelfth and Glencairn next day, and it seemed quite impossible that in the four remaining drives on Banchovie there should not be a bird at all.

Nor were these drives entirely blank. For though George had got all the grouse off the moor, it had not been an easy task to hold them, particularly certain old cocks and one or two headstrong youngsters. Shall we say that the Banchovie Lodge party that day killed all the seven grouse they shot at, and leave it at that?

"My dear fellows," said the General at six that evening, forgetting his rules for once and sinking his moustache in a very strong whiskey and soda, "I simply don't know what to say to you! I know the birds *were* there, and you saw them, didn't you, Michael, on Sunday? But from what they all say, there must have been an exceptional show of birds on Glencairn today and we ought to do all right tomorrow. I can't understand it, for neither the grit nor the heather nor the feeding generally are nearly as good as on Banchovie. But 3½ brace in a year like this and four blank drives . . . it's . . . it's simply *unbelievable*! Damn it, there's the telephone! Excuse me a moment!" He hurried out.

"Good evening, General!" It was the voice of the Angusburn tenant, who had the moor beyond Glencairn. "And what sort of a day did *you* have?"

"Oh, so-so!" muttered poor Sir Norman, blushing furiously into the telephone. "And how did you get on?"

"Oh, we didn't do too badly at all. 181½ brace, and that's a record for the moor, they tell me. What did you get? My keeper tells me your Glencairn beat was alive with birds when they went along your march, but we heard so little shooting from your side somebody said you must be using silencers!"

Silencers! as if the Blount-Garamies needed any such gangster equipment to help them make a bag of grouse! But still . . . 3½ brace! . . .

The General could only gurgle and blush down the telephone till he expected the vulcanite to burst into flame. He admitted that they had had a very poor day and talked vaguely of grouse migration, though he knew too well that by next morning the fiasco at Banchovie would be all over Aberdeenshire and Banffshire.

To fill his cup of sorrow to the brim, Mrs. MacLeish, his cook, appeared at that moment at the door leading from the kitchen to the hall. She was in a shocking temper for she had realized that Dugald, unnerved by disaster, had been at the bottle long before he reached home. She held in one hand all that was left of the grouse Mactavish, now plucked and drawn.

"Whatever hae ye been up to, General?" she said, holding up the wiry mangled frame. "Look at him! there's mair lead than meat in him and he's near as auld as Dugald. Did ye *all* shoot him and stamp on him afterwards? It's fifty years since Banchovie ever had to pluck auld wrecks like him on the Twelfth!"

But the General had fled; back in the smoking-room he was taking to the decanter as his outlawed ancestors had in old days taken to the hill.

It was in fact a dreadful evening, especially when the Kirkintoul stationmaster rang up to say he had "held" the London train for seven minutes and where were Dugald and the Banchovie birds? It was a bitter blow to admit that there were no Banchovie birds to send to London that evening, for the General had quietly counted on despatching a hundred brace at least to help defray his considerable expenses.

The one bright spot was the fact that Rupert Pilimore had passed on elsewhere before the party arrived home. He had left behind him a brief note of thanks and apology and a half-empty bottle of most questionable bath-salts in the General's bathroom, the odour of which affronted everyone for days. But he had gone, thundering off southwards in his low red car, and making no mention of the photographs. The whole lodge breathed a sigh of relief, but it was a very temporary one.

At 8.45, in the very middle of dinner, the General was summoned to the telephone.

"Say, is that you, General?"

"It's Sir Norman Blount-Garamie speaking."

"Good evening to you. Waal, General, I hear you've been had for suckers too?"

"What?"

"I'm told you've been sold a pup as well as me. I suppose it wouldn't interest you to sub-let your little allotment? I've had disease or something on mine, so I'm in the market."

"Oh, indeed."

"Name your price, Sir, and we might do a deal right now."

The General rang off. "Moor-coping", as Michael Arbuckle called it, especially over the telephone, always made him angry. It would have served these American upstarts right if he had named a price of £10,000 for the rest of the season and stuck to it. Only the thought of those waiting swarms of birds on Glencairn, and of his team, now nicely mellowed, prevented him.

The other result, even less welcome, of Rupert Pilimore's departure occurred when the illustrated papers arrived at the lodge on the following Saturday. There was nothing in *Sport and the Stage*, but in the *By-Prattler*, a much lower organ devoted to society gossip, whose jauntiness of tone had more than once stung General Garamie to the quick, appeared a half-page of photographs, admirably reproduced on glossy art paper and all too recognizable. Beneath them he read with horror:

"THE GLORIOUS TWELFTH. General Sir Norman Blount-Garamie and party on their way to the moors. From left to right. . . . (Inset right) Lord Charles Casserole enjoys a novel between the drives. (Inset left) The bag at luncheon. (Below) The scene at luncheon: Colonel Puddick tells a low one."

Poor Sir Norman! it will take him ten years to live that down in the Highlands. He had never believed it possible that anyone so negligible as Twittering Rupert could possibly have the last word.

XII

RED SKY IN THE MORNING

George awoke next morning to a rose-flushed dawn, which was quickly blotted out by a huddle of angry clouds and a rising wind from the east which swept at him over leagues of moor. He had no time to preen, but managed to snatch a cropful of heather and grit before Aunt Lizzie and he whirred away northwards to Glencairn, to shepherd the grouse over on to Banchovie. Had George known all that had happened overnight, he might have been quietly elated. But in the first hour of sunrise on the thirteenth, blown and famished and bedraggled, George realized to the full the stark hopelessness of his future. Exposed to all the fury of the elements, on this wretched diet of heather and water and tiny stones, he must fly all-whither without rest, until an eagle or a peregrine, a fox, or a shotgun, or disease claimed him in the end.

It was a forbidding prospect, but on one point George's mind was made up. He would give old N.B.G., confound him! and his carefully-picked team of assassins the two worst days they had ever imagined on one of the "best" moors in Scotland. He and Aunt Lizzie would make them a scorn and a hissing to all men by this simple device of local migration. The team would never guess what had happened, for the grouse would all be back on the beat next day. They might sack Dugald MacLeish and serve him right if they did, the treacherous ruffian, who professed to be a "keeper" of the game, who lived, that is, by lulling it into a state of false security, until the day of massacre dawned. And to think that George had been subscribing all these years to the Gamekeepers' Benevolent Association!

So thought George as he coaxed and bullied and hustled the Glencairn birds over the ridge on which he had sat during the first beat of the day before. Dark as the future might be, he would at any rate confound the General and Dugald and all their works.

General Garamie himself came down to breakfast that morning full once more of the calmly expectant confidence in the day's outcome which only once, in sixty years, had played him false. But as he stood before the fire and gulped down his porridge he looked at the weather with a tinge of anxiety, for his team had all rather broken training overnight in the shock of their disappointment. Crasher Casserole, in particular, had pink eyes, which made him with his sharp features and yellow-white hair even more ferret-like than usual. Though all his guns were exceptional performers, a strong wind would test even their skill, and there was always a danger of losing birds off the moor.

Crasher Casserole himself was not in the best of tempers as he breakfasted. To begin with, some oaf of a maidservant had tidied away

Murder in the Vestry, whose penultimate chapter he had been reading in the bath overnight, and though his lordship read seven or eight such novels in a week, he was feeling like a lioness robbed of her whelp. Worse still, Sammy Glemham and that old sharper Puddick had taken thirty shillings apiece off Nigel and himself overnight on some quite unpardonable hands, which had been aggravated by Nigel's finicking bids. Above all, there was a shortage of devilled bones at breakfast and he himself had drawn the last which had belonged, though he did not know it, to the grouse Mactavish. Somewhere among those aged and wiry thews he had nearly broken his plate on a pellet: privately he suspected someone of having been using swan-shot on the previous day.

Michael Arbuckle picked up a telegram from the side-table as he came in, read it, and said "Damnation!" with great emphasis.

"What's up, my dear fellow?" asked the General.

"It's Ben, my infernal huntsman. He's fallen over a blind place cubbing, and won't be able to ride for a month. That means I'll have to go down and hunt 'em myself. I haven't got a soul I can trust 'em to, bar Ben! Hell! and I'd meant to go on to the Duke next week!"

"You wouldn't have in any case! He's just put *me* off," said Nigel listlessly. He was picking at a herring with an air of profound gloom. "I got a letter this morning!"

He spoke very quietly though his whole soul was in torment, for he had sustained what was to him almost a mortal blow. The Duke, of course, had written very civilly saying how sorry he was to have to put off his house-parties for the time being on account of the illness of his wife, and hoping, etc. etc., a little later. This meant that poor Nigel Garamie was faced with a week entirely devoid of shooting engagements in the very middle of August in a bumper year. Nigel felt that *noblesse*, if nothing else, should have obliged the Duke, illness or no illness, to show a proper regard for highly important social functions of this kind, quite apart from the fact that unless moors were shot really hard in a bumper year, there was a serious risk of leaving too large a stock and getting disease. Blast! now Nigel would have to sit down and compose a letter of condolence to the Duke, just when he felt far more deserving of sympathy himself: for, as hinted before, he was a young man who took himself and his shooting very seriously indeed.

Only Lord Glemham and Colonel Puddick munched on imperturbably in silence. Both had been brought up in crack cavalry messes, in which it was not done either to think or speak at breakfast, and the habit had clung to them in after-life, even in a lodge where the morning papers never arrived till tea-time.

In the kitchen, with six loaders breakfasting at once, the atmospher was more than a trifle strained. John Tye and Colonel Puddick's man had done their best overnight in the bothy to drown Dugald's sorrows for him in two bottles of Glenlivet; they had kept him from suicide, but

Mrs. MacLeish had had to steer him up later to bed. She had saved up most of what she had intended to say to him for the morning, when Dugald would be in a riper condition to benefit from it, but lo and behold! he had got up at 4.30, while she was asleep, and had betaken himself to Glencairn to make certain that the birds were there. So Mrs. MacLeish's heavy batteries of remonstrance had had no opportunity to open fire. Dugald would probably have breakfast with Ian, whose cottage lay near the Glencairn road, and she might not see him all day.

As the guns came out of the lodge half an hour later to the waiting motor-cars, Sir Norman held out a little sheaf of numbered cards and each of his guests drew one. The cards bore the superscription "Banchovie Lodge, Aberdeenshire", and beneath in Sir Norman's neat handwriting the date, the beat, and the names of the guns in due order of social precedence. There was a space for the total bag and one for the gun's 'claim' for each drive. By this means at the end of the day Sir Norman could reckon up the bag against his guests' claims and have a useful cross-check against any purloining of game by beaters.

"Where's Nigel got to?" he asked when only two cards remained.

Michael Arbuckle smiled and murmured to Lord Glemham behind his hand: "Old Nigel's in the smoking-room casting his bread upon the waters."

Nigel came hurriedly out, drew his card, looked at the number and made a rapid mental calculation as he did so. Thank God! he had drawn No. 2, which meant that he would be No. 6 and in the famous top-butt in the third drive which was expected to be the most killing one of the day. Further, he would be No. 4 in the first drive after luncheon in a butt where the old Lord Billingham was once said to have killed 27½ brace.

Nigel had, by this time, almost recovered from the untimely blow dealt him by the Duke of Bolton. He had, ever since breakfast, really been "casting his bread upon the waters" and hoping to find it after not so many days. For in that time he had composed no less than three letters to friends as well as one telegram, discreetly glossing over the previous day's fiasco, but making it clear that the Duke, poor fellow! had "rather let him down", so that Nigel himself would be at a loose end from the 17th to the 23rd. To Nigel it was unthinkable that one of the best shots in Scotland should not be fully employed during that crucial week; unthinkable that there should be no one among all his carefully-garnered acquaintances who was not ready and eager to give him bed and board on condition that he killed as many of their grouse as possible. So now he had shot four arrows in the air, and it would not be his fault if one at least failed to score an invitation.

The cars roared out on to the road and headed up-hill for Glencairn under a sun which was struggling to force its way through stormy clouds. The wind was stronger than ever.

"I don't like the look of the weather," said the General solemnly to Charles Casserole and Colonel Puddick. "We shall need some straight powder today. You fellows will have to shoot as if your lives depended on it, to make up for yesterday."

Colonel Puddick rolled an eye upwards, "Yes, they'll take some stopping today."

66

"Yes," growled the other guest, "anything down-wind'll be worth a bit of money today. It's blasted cold too for August, ain't it?"

The cars stopped two miles on, not far from the end butt, where beside the road were waiting the loaders, Dugald, a flanker or two and old John Tye, with his sandy-red beard blowing in the wind and his three black and eager charges at his feet.

Dugald was looking a little less suicidal. He had come back, secretly very well satisfied, from his early reconnaissance. The grouse were there all right, in numbers, though they seemed rather restless and on the move: so much so that Dugald had scanned the heavens anxiously for any sign of an eagle. He had got back at seven in time for a shave and breakfast in Ian's cottage, assured that yesterday's appalling disaster was not likely to recur.

"Morning, Dugald, morning!" said the General heartily as the group stood up and touched their hats. "I hope you've got a grouse or two for these gentlemen today?"

"I'm hoping so," said Dugald, "there's a few birds on the moor."

The guns had hardly settled in their places when Colonel Puddick gave a low whistle and crouched in his butt. Far away a single black dot was skimming towards the butts with the speed of thought. This solitary bird, had they but known it, was none other than George himself. Greatly daring, and in defiance of Aunt Lizzie, he had once more forsaken his post and crossed to Glencairn, partly to make certain that all the grouse were off it, and partly to 'revisit his lost loves' and find out who they were. Not since his subaltern's days in the Boer War had George done such a daring personal reconnaissance in the presence of the enemy. Then, through inability to read a map, he had once found himself, all unwittingly and with all his men, in the very forefront of the battle and even beyond the cavalry screen. He had nearly got the D.S.O. for that until the truth leaked out, but since then he had been in no hurry to repeat such a performance. But this was a new George, feathered, weather-blown, hard as nails and possessed of a most vicious hatred of men and all they stood for in what he had once been wont so lightly to call the shooting-field.

So sixty yards from the butts, George braked suddenly and settled, with wings outspread, head up and feathered legs feeling for a landing. It was perfectly judged though he knew the risk he ran, for one of Sir Norman's favourite maxims was "Always shoot a settling bird. They only encourage other birds to settle near them and go back. If you take them just as they land with all their underparts exposed they are very vulnerable and you can kill them a longish way out."

But sixty yards was just too far even for Crasher Casserole, and George contrived to settle without scathe. In the depths of the heather he crouched and scuttled ten yards nearer the butts, and then very quietly drew himself erect behind a heather tuft. He could see Crasher Casserole in front of him with stout Colonel Puddick away on his left and Nigel Garamie's neat tweed cap in No. 2 butt on his right. The other butts George could not see, but he could guess who occupied them. Michael and the General he had seen on Sunday; the sixth must be Sammy Glemham, who for the last twelve years had been an honoured guest at Banchovie on the Twelfth. George knew that he was likely to remain so as long as he was lord of the manor of Sweatenham in Norfolk, for Sweatenham, as a game-preserve, was almost in a class by itself. All the other guns indeed owned what Nigel Garamie called "most useful" manors with the exception of Nigel himself, who relied for his invitations on auto-suggestion and a very high standard of marksmanship.

George could see at a glance that the three men in front of him were keenly alert and determined to lose no chances at the start of the drive by inattention. Even Crasher Casserole had returned to his pocket his new novel though, as claimed on the paper cover, it was "an exceptionally well-balanced family murder story" and had started with a most promisingly gruesome scene.

Erect and motionless, George stood behind his tuft and watched them unwinkingly for forty minutes while the beaters tramped two and a half miles of heather. He waited while expectancy changed to doubt, and doubt to bewilderment, and bewilderment to the bleak certainty that this also was going to be, in fact, already was, another blank drive. They hardly moved, they did not speak: their agony was silent. But as their tense watchfulness relaxed at last into fidgeting and sidelong glances towards their neighbours or at a stray pipit flitting over the butts, George's vicious hatred almost turned to pity. He guessed so well what they must be feeling.

Then he realized suddenly his own bitter lot and found himself hoping, most sincerely, that as soon as the drive was over, they would take Dugald out and put him up against a butt and shoot him out of hand.

So engrossed was George in watching this drama without words unfold itself in front of him that the line of beaters was within thirty yards of him almost before he knew it. He ducked down and scuttled back a few yards to the spot where he had landed, braced himself for a moment and then flung himself with his hoarse "G'back!" straight at the nearest beater, regardless of his shout and wildly-waving flag. But quick as he was, Crasher Casserole was quicker. He had had quite enough blank drives in the last twenty-four hours and he was not going to let this be one, if a grouse came within seventy yards of him. He let fly with his choke barrel almost as George left the ground, though perhaps the fact that a beater was as near as nothing in the line of fire, may have cramped him, ever so slightly, in his swing. Only five pellets on the very outside of the pattern hit George and plucked a cluster of downy feathers from under his stern. They stung George as he had not been stung since a day in his youth when he had "cut" a house-match to go to a race-meeting. The next instant he was over the beater's head and away for Banchovie.

The indignity of it, quite apart from the pain! To be peppered, as the phrase went, in his feathered behind, and by Crasher Casserole, of all people, to whom he himself had taught the secret of quick shooting. And to call it peppering! No one who had ever been shot there would describe such an atrocity by such a name: it was more like being branded with a red-hot iron. George had been twice severely wounded on active service, once in the Boer War when, on joining the Mounted Infantry, his Colonel had told him in front of the men exactly what he looked like on a horse; and once in the Great War, when they had opened the Scottish Church-hut at Rouen, and some dolt of a padre, nervous and hospitable, had upset a pot of scalding tea all over George's ankle. But gunshot wounds were clearly in a class by themselves.

George, as he skimmed and sidled away up the wind and put four hundred acres of heather between himself and his tormentors, was so angry that his eyes were blazing red when he landed close to Aunt Lizzie on the edge of the Pack.

"I heard them, George," she said grimly, "and it sairves ye right if they've hurt ye! Ye're a fule and an adder, though a'body kens auld cocks are ower daft. Never ye daur to dae the like again!"

69

XIII

THE THIRTEENTH

There are things, as someone has said, which cannot be put on the stage, and perhaps that thirteenth of August at Glencairn is one of them. It is impossible to picture the futility and the bewilderment with which the party came back to the luncheon-hut after the fourth drive. All that morning they had heard far away, in spite of the wind, the sound of other shooting-parties blazing away, freely and happily, on adjoining moors. But on Glencairn hardly a shot had broken the stillness. A snipe, three hares, and even a curlew which no one would ordinarily have considered worth a cartridge, comprised the morning's bag. The sun had gone in, the wind was still rising and it was as cold as mid-October. Worst of all, one of John Tye's young Labradors, brimming over with unslaked eagerness to show what he could do, had broken away after a hare and had coursed it over the hill out of sight in a manner more worthy of Altcar than Aberdeenshire. John Tye had departed blaspheming in pursuit of them, his sandy-red beard blowing in the breeze and his old bowler-hat crammed down to his ears, and had been away for nearly an hour.

Luncheon began in gloomy silence, though the General gradually drifted into a long-winded account of what had happened to a cousin of his in Roxburghshire in 1906; he had always discounted the phenomenon of grouse migration, and held it to be due, if indeed it existed at all, to bad keepering, poor heather or disease. But now his mind was grasping wildly at any excuse, however improbable, for the disaster of the morning.

His guests listened munching. They were interrupted by the sudden and unceremonious entry of John Tye, preceded by a gust of wind and the errant puppy, his deep-set eyes and purple tongue indicating that his chase and retribution had been stern.

"Yes, Tye?" said the General very drily. "We're in the middle of luncheon, you know." These rude Norfolk yokels were apt to jar on his feelings at times.

70

But old John was not to be denied. "Begging your pardon, General, and gentlemen," he squeaked, with a tug at the puppy and a dab at the brim of his bowler-hat. "But it's like this here. . . . My duzzy little dawg took me very near over to Banchovie afore I throshed him, and I never see so many grouse there in all my life! They wholly swahm and no mistake."

General Garamie gulped with amazement. "Well, Tye, that's what some of you said yesterday about this beat, but we've hardly seen a bird today. Are you *sure?*"

"Why, lor' love my bleeden heart alive, Sir," squeaked the old man, his voice rising still higher in his excitement, "du yu mean to say I don't know a grouse when I see one? Me and the dawg flushed 500 birds if we did one. I don't know no more'n a fule how they done it, but they've sucked us in properly, same as cock pheasants du. Yesterday, them birds was all over here and today they're all on Banchovie. That's a licker to me! But what we want to du now is to git right back there and suck them beggars in!" He paused. But for an "auxiliary", and an auxiliary from the South, to suggest a plan of operations to the General was an almost unheard-of proceeding.

"Thank you, Tye," said the General, still more drily. "I'll bear in mind what you suggest."

Tye touched his hat and let the puppy tow him out of the door, indignation bristling from his sandy beard.

"Well, if you ask me, Norman," said Lord Glemham slowly, when the door had shut, "old John's right. We're fools not to go where we know the birds are."

"But," moaned the General, "we've still four more drives to do on this beat, and they surely *can't all* be blank!" Sir Norman had lived all his life in accordance with King's Regulations, or Field Service Regulations, or the veteran wisdom of the Badminton Library, and never yet had these or the birds let him down. His moors had, with due allowance for the wind and the occasional shift of butts uphill or down, been driven more or less in the same way for seventeen years, Banchovie one day, Glencairn the next. It was the old way, the accepted way, the custom of his predecessors, the tradition of the moor. No birds had ever dared to flout that solemn ritual. There was, as always, a right way and a wrong way in which to do things. To change beats in the middle of a day's grouse-driving was almost like playing the Eton and Harrow match in September.

"But . . ." he began again, "the whole thing is quite against all I've been brought up to do!"

"Well, old John's usually pretty sound," said Lord Glemham. "We used to find at Sweatenham in January that once we started shooting on one beat, every cock pheasant disappeared after the first few shots. They're as cunning as foxes, however much they show up on a non-shooting day. We used to motor suddenly, beaters and all, from one beat to another and take 'em by surprise. And after all . . . you can't drive grouse for forty years and not expect them to learn *some* degree of self-preservation!"

"I don't like it," said the General. He was still wedded to routine. "It's not going to be easy to move the beaters there at a moment's notice."

The whole proposal, in fact, to him savoured more of a poaching foray than an ordered day's driving. For years his grouse had stayed on their proper beats to be shot at. For years they had been driven and flanked and pointed in to the self-same butts, so that he had been wont to say, "You can very nearly flank a grouse, if you know the ropes, down a drainpipe." For years the mountain had come uncomplainingly to Mahomet.

It was Nigel Garamie who made up the General's mind for him. Nigel had been feeling for the last twenty-four hours as if he had been almost visibly deflowered; he had in two days fired two cartridges and "divided" a snipe with Mark Puddick. No syndicate of bookmakers, or hail-fellow-well-met stockbrokers, lax and hearty, on a fifth-rate un-keepered moor could have done worse than this. There was not a house-party in Scotland, not a man among all his well-kept acquaintances, to whom Nigel could confide the stark truth of what had happened. Here he was, as fit as he had ever been, having fired 1000 rounds at clay pigeons at Merrivale to get his eye well in, for what? He and his fellow *virtuosi* had arrived, trained to the minute, with all their instruments well tuned, ready and eager to play, and the curtain had risen on an almost empty theatre. Nigel felt like a National favourite who has cut a voluntary at the first fence or a member of the Quorn who has somehow let himself in, in November, for a day's rabbiting.

Yet . . . three good drives on the other beat this afternoon and Flodden might yet be Bannockburn. Nigel felt he could shoot as if his life depended on it as, indeed, socially it did. "I think John Tye's right,

Norman," he said slowly. "We had better go where the grouse are. It is not ours, er, to reason why."

These simple heroic words turned the scale.

"Nigel's right," said Mark Puddick, filling his mouth with cheese and ramming in a stick of celery after it. "If the beggars have stolen a march on us, we'd better go over there and have a crack at 'em. I'm all for it!"

Poaching or no poaching, the whole party felt that for once Mahomet must go to the mountain. Watches were synchronized, the beaters set out across the ridge to the Black Strath beat which lay nearest to Glencairn, and the guns and loaders motored round by the road.

XIV

ON THE BLACK STRATH

It was Aunt Lizzie, who was on patrol with George between Glencairn and the Banchovie beat who first saw the beaters suddenly appear over the hill and spread out facing southwards.

"They've kenned our hidey-hole, the muckle sons of shame! What'll we do, George?"

But George's blood was up. "There's only one thing for it. Get 'em all together in the middle of the strath and then fly straight at the beaters. Tell 'em" (his mind was groping back confusedly among the football maxims of his youth) "to make for the corner flag!"

So as the beaters lined out and halted till it was time to start, from covey to covey, from pack to pack the two old grouse sped on their errand of warning.

The drive was across the wind, which was by this time nearly a gale, so strong that Ian threw eight of his best men far forward on the downwind side to flank the birds in. The General needed no persuasion to forget about the draw and put his three strongest guns, Crasher Casserole, Nigel and Michael Arbuckle, in the three lowest butts. It was clear from the moment they took their places that the moor was alive with birds: one great lot rose with a roar off the ridge which masked the butts and went back into the drive; and a host of birds in ones and twos kept rising and following them. From where he was in the top butt, the General could see a little ridge a mile and a half away, and over and along it streamed from minute to minute scores of little black dots, like midges, which meant grouse coming into the centre of the beat.

"By Gad, Tom!" he exclaimed to his loader. "Old Tye was right! I never saw so many grouse. Have we got enough cartridges, do you think?"

"I've got 120 here, sir," said Tom, "and we can get at the other bag before the next drive. They should do us!"

The guns waited in tense silence, eyes roving along the ridge, safety-catches forward, each loader stooping behind them with the second gun and two more cartridges held in the knuckles of the right hand. Here was the team in action, knowing exactly what to do, determined to show in this far corner of Aberdeenshire what its training and lifelong experience could accomplish as soon as, in Dugald's phrase, "the trouble began".

From the top butt the General could see the waving flags of three beaters come over the far ridge and sink out of sight towards him. He knew that somewhere in that great cauldron of heather and peathags which was the Black Strath there must be hundreds of grouse collecting or moving forward. They would appear suddenly as dark and onrushing targets, bursting over the rim of the cauldron in front of him.

He waited; then he heard far away on the down-wind side a great outburst of shouting, Highland voices upraised in shrill remonstrance. The General fumed, for his beaters had the strictest orders never to shout, but only to use their flags. Shouting was the sign of a "bad" moor, run by amateurs. "I loathe shouting and disorder," he was wont to say. It had always pained him that at Ascot or Epsom even the best people sometimes gave audible vent to their excitement at the end of a race. A true gentleman kept silence whether he was killing birds or watching one of his horses lose him twenty thousand pounds.

The shouting went on, wilder and more incessant. Then far down over the curve of the moor and from somewhere in front of the lower butts, he heard two shots, a pause, two shots again, and then a flurry of shots for two or three minutes. He crouched even more tensely. Then suddenly in perfect alignment the flags of the beaters broke over the little ridge seventy yards away. With a sick feeling at his heart and long white fingers relaxing their hold on the fore-end of his gun,

74

General Garamie realized that the drive was over and neither he nor the three guns he could see below him had fired a single shot.

It was Michael Arbuckle in the bottom butt, whose long career of hunting foxes had made him quick-witted and adaptable, who had saved the drive from being a blank one. From where he was the little ridge in front of the line of butts hid him from the beat, but he

guessed, from the storm of shouting, that grouse must be breaking out down the wind. As none came forward he slipped out of his butt and down the gully, and once clear of the line ran forward as hard as he could towards the nearest flanker. As he came over the rise, he could see the complete half-circle of beaters and hundreds of grouse, in twos and threes and coveys, pouring over the flags at the lower end.

Michael's second horseman, who loaded for him, was panting along twenty yards behind with his great bag of cartridges rattling and clumping on his back. The flanker, Dugald MacLeish himself, dropped into the heather as Michael came up and furled his flag.

"The moor's bewitched!" he moaned. "There's no a bird gone right the day!"

"Then stand up, man, and wave your ruddy flag like blazes," said Michael. "Perhaps they'll think I'm a beater too!"

Apparently they did: for three brief ecstatic minutes Michael, bolt upright beside the old keeper, was shooting as hard as he could at birds which swept straight at the flag. There were not many left by that time but the scared, the lazy and a few scattered old cocks remained. Michael killed 6½ brace of what he called "real screamers" in fifteen cartridges before the drive ended.

XV

THE LAST DRIVE

The moment the drive was over, the General called what he described as a council of war. Dugald, with tears now running down his face, was repeating wildly that the moor was bewitched. His grouse, his reputation, the record of the moor, perhaps his job, and certainly the radio set (which he had secretly counted on buying with the tips after this party had left the lodge) all seemed to have gone west together. Five of the team had not even "fleshed their guns" and, as Ian Murdoch said: "There's a thousand birds gone wrong, if there's one!" Nigel Garamie's gloom was more pronounced than ever; he felt that insult had been added to the grave injury already done him, and even broke training so far as to allow himself a cigarette.

Lord Glemham, sitting apart on his shooting-seat, had a low-voiced conversation with old John Tye. The latter, a keeper bred from generations of Norfolk poachers, was undismayed.

"What we want to du now, m' lord," he squeaked, "is same as we did at Sweatenham that time last year when we druv all them woods blank into the brick-pits and put the guns on the hind side of the brushers. We sucked all them birds in properly when they went back. Them cock pheasants get to know which is a brusher, like, and which ain't, and I reckon these here grouse-birds are the same!"

A little way away Dugald and the General and Ian Murdoch were

76

conferring with Nigel and Charles Casserole. Dugald quite frankly said he did not know what to do. He had in the past met, unshaken, the worst vagaries of weather and disease, the geographical problems of his moors, the whims of unreasonable owners, and guns who could not shoot, but this time the grouse themselves seemed to be against him. They had always played into his hands, but what on earth was a keeper to do on a moor where the grouse took active and intelligent steps to avoid destruction?

Lord Glemham left John Tye and conferred at length with Sir Norman and Nigel and Michael Arbuckle. Then the whole party, beaters and loaders and guns, turned and tramped off westwards through the heather.

"I don't like it! I don't like it!" Sir Norman kept repeating. "I've had this moor for seventeen years and we've never done it that way yet!"

"I dare say, Sir," said Michael, "but you must remember the grouse never have either!"

"Well, my dear fellow, I grant that, but . . . with this wind we shall be having the birds clean off the moor if we're not careful!"

"Well, Norman," said Lord Glemham, "there's always that risk in a wind, but it seems a pity now that we're all here and know the next beat's swarming with birds, not to have a try for them."

"Well," said Sir Norman, "one last drive then, and if we can't get on terms with them, we'll go home!"

The party trailed along rather forlornly, for most of them had not walked after grouse for thirty years. A stinging shower of rain blew them along the moor. They turned up their collars and walked in silence except Michael and John Tye, whose cheerfulness no weather and no misfortune could damp. It had been John Tye's suggestion to do what they were attempting now. The Tulchan beat, into which most of the birds had just flown off the Black Strath, ended in a huddle of low hills which formed the western march of Banchovie moor. The beaters were to line out along the march, with the guns between them, and beat towards the line of empty butts, crossing on their way the Tulchan burn which cut north and south between steep banks and across the beat a mile from the march. Here the guns would stop and await the grouse if they came back over the beaters on the wind.

George and Aunt Lizzie, crouching in the heather with their heads

"— . . . for most of them had not walked after grouse
for thirty years."

towards the wind and their eyes half-closed against the sting of the blown rain, saw the party trailing along the ridge four hundred yards away. Surely old N.B.G. was not going to drive the Tulchan beat in the teeth of the wind? With the rain-drops glistening on his horny beak, George could not count the party and he did not discern that some of them were carrying guns.

"Same old tactics, I suppose, Lizzie?" he said. "Make for the corner flag, eh? Back over the sticks?" George, despite the rain and the aching of his wound, felt almost uplifted. He had given old N.B.G. a cracking bad day, and now the weather had come to help him. If they tried a silly drive like that, every bird would go back over the beaters, for all now recognized that there was little to fear. Of the grouse who had flown at Michael in the last few minutes of the Black Strath drive, not one had lived to tell the tale among the others on the Tulchan. But Aunt Lizzie was thinking of the Muckle Gale which, three seasons before, had blown her up from the Borders. This screaming east wind reminded her of that awful evening.

"Aye, George," she said. "But we maun keep low and fly through them. If yon wind gets under our tails, we'll be awa' beyond Loch Ness and intil the sea, maybe. Awa' with us noo and warrn them a'!"

As they sped on their mission, George thought he had never seen so many grouse in his life. The moor was black with birds, all feeding as if their lives depended on it, for they sensed what was coming, a night of storm and rain which they would have to endure, crouched tail to tail, with what little protection was afforded by the lie of the sodden ground. There were birds here from the Black Strath and hundreds of strange birds from Glencairn, restless and anxious to get back to the moor they knew. But George, as a prophet, was now beginning to convince his hearers. He had no time to think of the forlorn hope, drenched and gloomy, that had disappeared westwards along the ridge. Had he done so, he might have felt with pride that his desire to confound them, to make them suffer ignominy and frustration, and to tramp miles for nothing, was almost accomplished.

Guns and beaters spread out below the march and began to move slowly eastwards in the teeth of the gale. Far in front a few grouse rose and skimmed, battling with the wind, towards the centre of the beat. As they reached the Tulchan burn, the guns and loaders stopped and took post under its eastern bank which gave them some slight concealment, both from the gale and from approaching birds. The beaters led by Dugald and Ian moved slowly on, their flags erect, towards the centre of the beat. There Aunt Lizzie and George and Sir Euan sat on a little knoll and looked from the swarms of feeding birds below and all round them to the flags advancing a mile away. More and more birds rose and skimmed up-wind towards them and joined the great assembly.

"Let's get them a' together," said Aunt Lizzie, "and we'll a' gang west at once. If we dinna keep the puir things together and well doon, we'll be oot o' control and intil the sea, I'm thinkin' ''. The old hen's knowledge of the geography of Scotland was limited, but the sea, she guessed, was always the ultimate danger for a bird that could not stop.

The beaters trudged on, leaning against the gale, their minds a blank. They had nearly done their job and earned their pay, and it mattered little to them if "the gentlemen" felt frustrated. If they did shoot a few grouse, well, the glen would never see them: they would be eaten in the big house or London, maybe, and in a day or two the gentlemen would all disappear for some other moor, and Banchovie would be quiet in the sunshine till the house filled again with a rather weaker team of guns for "the second time over", and so on till October. Their job was beating, at 8/6 a day and their "piece" for dinner, and maybe a dram at the big house in the evening.

Sir Euan and Aunt Lizzie, bolt upright and motionless on their knoll, sent George scuttling off to whip in a few stragglers. They looked down at the great congregation of crouching birds which covered the heather all around them.

"Now!" said Sir Euan when the beaters were a hundred yards away, and launched himself with a hoarse "G'rr back" straight at the advancing line.

There was a roar like thunder of over three thousand wings as the grouse leapt simultaneously from the heather. As John Tye said later to a crony in the Sweatenham Arms: "The moor fair riz at us and come ascreechen. Them birds properly bid us defiance! That was like all the geese getting up on Holkham Sands." Dugald, who had not ceased to believe that the moor was bewitched, felt as if every grouse in Aberdeenshire was bearing down on him, low and black as evil, with menace in its wings. Young Donald Murdoch, aged eleven, who was out for the first time, gave a scream and fell flat in the heather, and Dinah, the "young bitch", turned head over heels in terror and legged it blindly for her kennel. The beaters shouted and waved their flags furiously, as if to defend themselves against the rush of fifteen hundred maddened birds. This was like Birnam Wood coming to Dunsinane: it was the very spirit of the moor in revolt.

Led by Sir Euan and Aunt Lizzie, the great assembly was through the line of shouting beaters in a second. For all Aunt Lizzie's injunctions to "keep low", the pace was terrific and half the birds were soon out of control. At nearly a hundred miles an hour they swept on westwards towards the burn. Suddenly a line of dark figures sprang to life in front of them. Too late Aunt Lizzie realized that the treacherous pop-eyed bogles had once more played her false and were in their hidey-holes again. She zoomed ten feet in the air and accelerated to her last ounce of speed and swerve.

George, who had risen last and was struggling to keep up with the Pack, as well as his wound and stiffness would let him, suddenly saw the leading flyers thirty yards ahead shoot upwards and sideways, and as they did so Aunt Lizzie and Sir Euan crumpled and fell. At the same moment shots rang out all along the line of the burn, as Sir Norman's team came into action at last.

With the wind under his tail and the rush of the great assembly of terrified birds sweeping him on, George made no attempt to stop or turn. He was like a steeplechase horse who sees the leaders fall at the last jump but merely quickens his pace and strides at the fence as if it was not there. Damn them once again! the bastards had tricked him when he thought he had put it across them for the day. Then, horrifically enlarging on his vision and little more than ten yards in front of him, he saw the face of Crasher Casserole, his old rival, peering intently over the bank of the burn, almost on a level with his own.

It was Crasher, all right. The thin, pink, ferret-like features, the keen malignant eyes were fixed implacably on George himself, as with a deft half-turn he handed his empty gun to his loader and simultaneously grasped the other one. George could see he was doomed; at the pace the grouse were coming, not streaming but spread out in an immense phalanx half a mile wide, Crasher could not hope to take another bird in front of him. But he would turn with ease and shoot George in the back the moment he had passed, and probably some other wretched bird as well. George felt in his already aching loins the thin intolerable pain, the sudden shock of helplessness, the crash with which he would hit the stony ground, and roll over and over in a flurry of loosened feathers, to lie still until some dog gripped him and lifted him and bore him back, slavering and triumphant, to his master. That would be George's end: and all his epitaph would be that he was just half a brace of "real good birds" bagged in a down-wind drive in Aberdeenshire.

George's blood boiled suddenly. Not on his life! He put his left wing down, banked for the merest fraction of a second, and then, with the last ounce of ferocity that was in him, hurled himself into the pink and staring face of his enemy. There was a crash and George knew no more.

The grouse, now with no master but the gale, poured away westwards, rising higher and higher, till they were lost to sight among a mass of dark and lowering clouds.

XVI

AFTERMATH

There has been a good deal of ill-informed speculation about the shocking accident on the Banchovie Moor, in which Lord Charles Casserole was knocked senseless by a driven grouse, and in falling fatally injured with his second gun both his loader and Captain Nigel Blount-Garamie, who was forty yards away. The *Evening Siren* indeed, ever in the van of sensation, momentarily shelved all reference to Hitler and Czechoslovakia behind banner headlines which announced:

"Grouse K.O's Peer. Fatal Affray on Moor."

But then, as Michael Arbuckle informed their "special grouse-shooting representative", when he called hot-foot at the lodge, they could nearly always be relied upon to get hold of the wrong end and paint it purple.

The procurator-fiscal, with an even more limited experience of high-class grouse-driving, brought in a verdict of "Death by Misadventure", with a rider that the custom of allowing a retainer to hold a fully-loaded firearm in close proximity to his master's back seemed to him a very dangerous one, and likely to cause serious accidents. And the *Squire*, in a leading article entitled "Perils of the Shooting Field", went further and suggested that as his lordship was a very well-known and most experienced sportsman, the unfortunate loader might conceivably have shot himself in the flurry of the moment, and lamented the irreparable

loss of Capt. Garamie, one of the most brilliant shots among the younger generation.

And on a score of moors men, who should have known much better, lit their pipes after luncheon and murmured to one another:

"Extraordinary show that was of poor old Crasher, wasn't it? Well, I can't say I was altogether surprised. A brilliant shot, I grant you, but he's always struck me as a very *keen* one, don't you know?"

And as Lord Charles had sustained a broken nose and very severe concussion, he was quite unable to throw any light on the tragedy itself.

Perhaps the most curious feature of the whole affair was that the grouse which had been responsible for so many sad consequences was never apparently picked up. Ian and Allan Fraser, the policeman, and the special representative of the *Evening Siren* searched for it for a whole morning, as the procurator-fiscal wanted it as an exhibit. It must have been, in the latter's own words, "what sporting-men term a runner bird". But from the two feathers found wedged in Lord Charles's denture, which were of course promptly submitted to experts, it was unquestionably an adult male. Luckily, however, the abrupt ending of the Czechoslovakian close-season, and the Munich crisis which followed it, diverted men's attention to what Michael described as "somewhat bloodier themes".

Poor Sir Norman Garamie let both Glencairn and Banchovie, on the day after the accident, to a syndicate of Americans; and in the Court of King's Bench in 1939, it was held that at the material time, defendant could not possibly have been aware that there was hardly a grouse on either beat, and the doctrine of *caveat emptor* must clearly be held to be applicable. While far away in Western Inverness-shire the stalking on one of our best-known deerforests was temporarily ruined by a vast influx of grouse which moved uneasily, in locust swarms, from hill to hill and displayed all the shyness and native cunning of a flock of rooks.

.   .   .   .   .

If you are ever in the Qu'hais' Club in May or June, you may sometimes see at the head of the stairs a frail, pale old gentleman with reddish eyebrows and a rather commanding nose, who is leaning on a rubber-tipped stick and asking a waiter if he would be so good as to bring him a glass of barley-water to the Silence Room. He has, you will gather, come up from Cambridgeshire for the Chelsea Flower Show or possibly the Empire Garden Party at Hurlingham. He will discourse to you eagerly, if you let him, on the subject of roses or gladioli, and the dower-house garden at Five Mile Wallop has clearly more than a local reputation both among horticulturists and as a bird sanctuary. He is, as he will tell you, arranging shortly for a "ramble" on his property by the local branch of the Society for the Protection of Birds, though he is not always able to accompany his guests owing to sciatica, the result, you gather, of an old hip-wound.

This old gentleman, as the waiter will confirm, is none other than Colonel the Honourable George Hysteron-Proteron, C.B., who was many years ago among the most renowned game-shots in the Kingdom ... though, since his serious illness in 1938, from which he so miraculously recovered after being unconscious for a fortnight in a nursing home, his doctor does not permit the subject of shooting to be mentioned. The Club servants are all very fond of him, for it is a club with a high proportion of very exacting members (many of them with livers indurated by prolonged association with the East). But the Colonel alone hardly ever has a word of complaint to make, and he always acts as a brake on intemperate discussion in the Club; for, as he is never tired of remarking:

"So much depends upon one's point of view. *I* always try to put myself in the other fellow's place!"